THE FALL AND

REDEMPTION OF

SHADOWMERE

I

THE FALL AND REDEMPTION OF SHADOWMERE

A PARABLE AND COMMENTARY ON CHRIST'S VICTORY OVER DARKNESS AND THE CALL TO DISCIPLESHIP

MATT BOHLMAN

Copyright

Dedication

To Christ, the "Marshal over all," and to my parents, Larry and Vicky Bohlman, for being faithful "deputies" of His light and love all these years.

Preface: Why read this book?

(1) What does it mean to be a *disciple* of Jesus and not just a *convert*?

(2) What are the tactics of Satan to take us out of the fight?

(3) Was the death of Jesus an accident or a Divine plan to wage war against powers of darkness?

(4) What does it mean to say Jesus bore our sins on the cross, and why did He enter the realm of death to defeat it?

(5) What does it mean to speak of God redeeming and rescuing us from the domain of sin and Satan?

To deal with these questions and more, this book will take two approaches: **Story** and **Commentary.**

We live in a time when Christian theology often gets reduced to memorizable soundbites of doctrine. We have lost the power of the parable to pierce the heart with the transformative truth of the gospel. Set within the context of the "Wild West" frontier, this short story will challenge both teens and adults to revisit the death and resurrection of Christ and rediscover what it means to be a disciple—a "deputy" of Christ's authority over darkness.

At the end, interested readers are encouraged to explore the true nature of spiritual warfare in our day, followed by an invitation to take a "deep dive" into the Bible and behold the theological beauty and wonder of the cross as victory over sin and powers of darkness.

Table of Contents

Helpful introduction: Who was the serpent in the Garden of Eden?

This story will refer to a spiritual being called the "serpentine *nachash.*" This is rooted in the opening verses of the third chapter in Genesis. In the Garden of Eden, we encounter a mysterious being, a "serpent" according to many English translations. In Hebrew the word is *nachash.* Scholars have noted, however, that the Hebrew root of *nachash* allows for three different meanings. As a noun it means "serpent." As a verb it means "diviner" or "deceiver." As an adjective it can mean "shining." These three meanings would have signaled to the ancient reader that the *nachash* serpent of Eden is an angelic being belonging to the highest ranks of the seraphim (Isaiah 6:1-2) and part of God's heavenly host council. For in Hebrew the word "seraph," when used as a noun, can also mean "flying serpent." In the Ancient Near East, we find similar accounts describing heavenly, throne guardians that had a serpentine appearance.

All of this helps us to understand that the Garden of Eden was not a private resort for Adam and Eve. Rather, it was God's earthly sanctuary and throne—His temple. Much of Genesis and the rest of the Bible comes into sharper focus when we realize the deceiving "serpent" in Eden may have taken on the temporary form of a snake, but his true nature was much greater. He was an angelic seraph who rebelled against heaven's plan for God's human image-bearers to rule the earth (Genesis 1:28). He is later identified as Satan, meaning "adversary," and is also called "the accuser of the brethren"(Revelation12:9).

Chapter 1

"Then the Lord God said to the serpent [nachash]...'He will strike your head, and you will strike His heel'"(Genesis 3:15).

"You know that He was revealed so that He might take away sins, and there is no sin in Him...The Son of God was revealed for this purpose; to destroy the Devil's works" (1 John 3:5;8).

"Then Jesus spoke to them; 'I am the light of the world. Anyone who follows Me will never walk in the darkness but will have the light of life'" (John 8:12).

I t wasn't long ago that the dusty streets of a small town in the Old West crisscrossed the battle lines of heaven. The town was called Shadowmere, and in Shadowmere is where this story begins. It was a homely town, as small towns tend to be. It had a saloon, a general store, a bank, and a recently opened hotel, but otherwise was unremarkable and plain.

It was summer time, and the afternoon sun hung low overhead as carriages cluttered through the dusty streets. People bustled back and forth, each going about their daily routines. It was shaping up to be nothing more than another ordinary day. But unknown to everyone, an ominous, black serpent was slowly slithering its way toward the unsuspecting. It was in no rush. Time had long ago been forgotten. Through the tall weeds it glided without a sound. At the edge of town, it came upon a nest of sleeping hens, but the serpent paid them no mind. It had not come for hens. It slithered past the horse stable, along the side of the bank, and then slipped quietly under the boardwalk. Upon reaching the rough, hewn steps that led into the saloon, it stopped, coiled its long body into a tight ball, and waited.

The black serpent, curled under the steps, was no ordinary snake. It was a serpentine *nachash*, a powerful and cunning spirit-being as old as pebble and stone. Though not eternal, it witnessed the day the mighty Ancients spoke the earth into existence. And it was present when the Ancients breathed life and spirit into human imagers and decreed to all heavenly, spirit-beings, "These created imagers are my children. They shall rule this earth and prove themselves worthy of even greater rule in the next age."

But the *nachash* serpent disapproved, for it secretly coveted the earth for its own rule. Thus, it sought to challenge the wisdom of the Ancients. It protested loudly to the council of heaven, "The Ancients' children are weak! They cannot be trusted with such honor!"

Some within the council of heaven were persuaded by the words of the serpent, for the serpent's words were crafty and enchanting. But the Ancients remained unpersuaded and refused to change their edict. "Our children bear the mark of Our image," they decreed. "What is given to them will not be taken away."

The serpent hissed at the Ancients. In response, lightning flashed and thunder cracked. The serpent flinched and backed down. But it did not repent. On that day, the serpent departed from the Divine light of the Ancients—never to return.

Over time, the serpent's fangs grew long and sharp, and the soft underbelly of its skin thickened with hard callouses. Its very nature twisted and bent until it became warped into a repulsive, hideous strength. Far removed from the light of the Ancients, its very insides soon began to fester and rot into pools of poisonous, dark venom.

Hatred of the Ancients and their children consumed it. "I shall shame the rule of the Ancients and their human imagers with my own rule," it swore. "The Ancients may have no beginning, but my rule will have no end!"

Unwilling to let go of its covetous desire for the earth, a great war broke out upon the earth between the serpent and the children of the Ancients. Generations came and went. Some of the Ancients' children fought hard against the serpent, while others fell prey to its venom.

The strategy of the serpent was always the same: to strike first, then withdraw, and watch its venom turn the Ancients' children against each other. And so it was that the battle came to Shadowmere.

The town banker had just closed up and was walking along the boardwalk. He was a stout man, who carried himself with a high degree of importance. He tipped his hat at a young lady passing by and licked his lips. His mouth was dry. He took out his watch and glanced at it. Having a few minutes to spare before his wife expected him home, he decided to walk across the street to the saloon.

The serpent watched as the banker approached. Its scaly, black hide remained in a tight corkscrew until just the right moment. As the banker's foot hit the first step, the serpent uncoiled and struck. Its fangs pierced through the banker's black boots into his skin. Hot venom rushed into the wound as the banker cried out in pain. No sooner had the serpent struck, than it recoiled itself and waited again.

Footsteps pounded on the boardwalk above. The town blacksmith and the storekeeper rushed down the saloon steps, unaware of the danger lurking in the shadows. Immediately, the serpent struck again—once, twice! Both men fell to the ground and began to writhe in agony. The serpent then opened its mouth wide, and from deep inside it hissed out puffs of hot, black breath into the swirling dust. Like tiny, wispy eggs, they floated through the air and slipped into the ears of the banker, blacksmith, and storekeeper.

"Three should be enough for now," the serpent whispered and slithered further back into the shadows to watch the inevitable unfold. Within seconds, the three men lying on the ground began to snarl at each other. Each blamed the other for their pain. The saloon door swung on its hinges. Soon a small crowd of people gathered around its victims as they continued to writhe on the ground, clawing at their boots.

The storekeeper's wife rushed forward. From under the steps, the serpent watched as she bent down to take the boot off of her husband. "Don't touch me, woman!" he screamed. Then, without warning, the storekeeper lurched his head up and angrily sank his teeth into his wife's arm, spitting the serpent's venomous infection into her flesh. With a cry of pain, she fell back. People frantically wrestled to pull her husband off her. Almost immediately she began to snarl like the others.

"Get away from me, you vermin!" she shrieked.

An older gentleman mistakenly stepped on the woman's hand. Like a viper she struck out, biting and scratching those closest to her.

"Goooood. Yessss," the serpent hissed. "So easily they fall."

Five infected people quickly became ten, which soon turned into twenty. Within minutes, the center of town became a thrashing pit of screaming, clawing, and biting.

"And so, it begins," the serpent chuckled. Nothing delighted the serpent more than seeing its victims turn against each other and take on its nature. As the chaos spread, it slipped out from its hiding place, sniffed the air, and began searching out townspeople not yet infected. No one was spared. All the while, the serpent continued to hiss a string of wispy eggs into the air. There appeared to be no hope for Shadowmere.

Just when all seemed lost, two mysterious outriders rode into town on shimmering, white horses. Sensing a hostile presence, the serpent whirled around. "Noooo!" it shouted. "It cannot be!"

But it was. The Ancients stepped down from their horses. Father and Son, they stood before the swirling mass of human misery. The Son turned to the Father. Neither said a word at first. The Father reached for his Son's neck and pulled him close. He felt a small tremor, a slight shudder, begin to course through his Son's body. "Steady, Son. Steady, now," he whispered.

The Son bent down and pressed his ear against the heart of the Father. From deep inside, the rhythm of the universe could be heard. He closed his eyes and focused on the sound. His breathing began to calm. Once his heart beat in unison with his Father, he stood back up. "It is time," he said. "We are One."

"We are One," the Father affirmed. A final embrace and the Father released him. The Son set his face like flint and turned on his heel to face the fallen townspeople.

He walked quickly over to the person nearest him and searched for the wound where the serpent's venom entered their body. Without hesitation he began to suck the dark poison out of the wound, taking it into himself. He then walked over to a second victim and did the same, then a third person followed by a fourth and so on. Some of the townspeople, lost in their madness, attacked the Son as he sought to heal them. They bit him on his head, his back, his hands, and his feet. But their attacks against him became the source of their own healing. With each bite, the venom was pulled out of their bodies and became absorbed into the flesh of the Son.

Throughout the nightmarish trauma unfolding before him, the Father remained standing at a distance unmoved but not unaffected. Huge tears welled up in his eyes as he watched his much-loved Son absorb the brutality of those attacking him. But surprisingly, the Father did not intervene to stop their attack.

His Son, weakened by the onslaught of the townspeople, stumbled and fell, but he did not stop. He pressed on. When a person was healed, their eyes would clear and their minds would be restored. One by one, he drew the poison out of each person until all were healed.

Upon seeing the Son reverse its poison, the serpent became enraged. "Why now!" it wailed. "Why this place? No matter! He is before me in the weakness of human flesh. Never before has the Prince of heaven been so vulnerable to me. The time to strike him down is now!"

With fury, the serpent reared back and struck the Ancient Son. Again and again, it lashed out—each bite pumping deadly venom into the Son. But the Son did not fight back or attempt to defend himself. Like a lamb led to the slaughter, he did not cry out or struggle to escape. Although the Son was clothed in human skin, the serpent began to perceive there was something unique about the Son's humanity—something even its darkest venom could not overcome. With each strike, the serpentine *nachash* sensed its venom was rapidly being depleted. Before it could slither away to regather its strength, a strong hand suddenly reached out and gripped it firmly behind the head.

The strength of the hand upon its neck was unbelievable—stronger than any force it had ever encountered. The serpent vigorously struggled to twist its scaly head around to attack this new threat, when to its horror, the face of the Ancient Father appeared. The serpent's shifty, impish eyes widened in fear as it stared into eyes that blazed brighter than a thousand suns. Frantically, it tried to avert the burning gaze of the Ancient Father, desperate for darkness and shadows.

"Let me go! Release me!" it screamed.

Instead the hand squeezed tighter, choking off its shrieking demands. Like a mighty crashing wave, the voice of the Father thundered, "The doom of your judgment has come! Now you shall be plundered and pillaged!" The serpentine *nachash* felt its mouth pried open wide. To its shock, the Father crushed its head down onto the heel of his only Son. Its fangs, dripping with venom, sank deep into the soft flesh of the Son.

The Father then gripped its tail and ran his hand firmly along the length of its scaly hide.

The serpent felt the deep reservoirs of its poisonous venom being squeezed out. With sheer terror the serpent realized too late the Ancients' secret plan of attack. The Son had come in human form to lure it into a trap. Its venom had never failed to defile, corrupt, and condemn the Ancients' children. But its powers of defilement were powerless against the Son's purity. Since its venom could not corrupt or turn the Son against the Father, the Son was using his own life to drain it dry. Once done, the Ancients' children would have a share in the Son's life. *It must not happen!*

Desperately, the serpent twisted and turned, but its struggles were of no use. The grip upon its neck was like an iron vice, able to crush a planet if it so desired. Every attempt to wiggle free forced more poisonous venom out of its fangs and into the Son.

After the last, remaining drop of venom was drained away, the Father wrenched the serpent's head from the heel of his Son. He then reached into the serpent's gaping mouth and grabbed hold of both of its fangs. Again the serpent's eyes widened in fear "Nooooooo!" it shrieked. But its sniveling cry was cut short by a sickening sound. "*SNAP! SNAP!*"

The Father calmly pocketed the broken off fangs of the serpent and leaned in close to whisper to it. "And you thought you could rise above the heights of *my*

9

heaven? You are as foolish as you are rebellious. I leave you with nothing but your foul, forked tongue."

With great strength, the Father then hurled the serpent's twisted body high into the air. It fell hard and slammed into the dirt.

Fangless and venomless, it slowly slithered away into the tall grass, defeated and whimpering.

Chapter 2

The legs of the Son buckled under him, and he collapsed into his Father's waiting arms. His chest rose and fell as he gasped for air, each breath further apart than the one before. Both knew he was dying. "Dad—is it over? Is every drop gone?"

"Yes, my Son. You did well. You were so strong." Tears coursed down the Father's cheeks and fell upon his Son's chest.

A look of calm settled on the Ancient Son's face. "It is finished." A mysterious wind suddenly swept down from the hills, swirled around them, and carried away the Son's last breath. With a cry, the Father buried his face into the crumbled form held in his arms. A still quiet descended upon Shadowmere, and all that could be heard was the faint weeping of a mourning Father.

The Ancient Father then did something strange, which many townspeople to this day continue to discuss. He pulled out a pure, white thread and dipped it three times into a bloody wound over his Son's heart. Tying the blood-stained thread around the serpent's fangs, he then looped it like a necklace around the head of his Son. With the serpent's fangs resting upon his Son's chest, the Father stood up.

"These instruments of death now belong to you, my Son. No more shall they threaten to bring eternal ruin upon those who share in our life."

Stooping down, he picked up the limp body of his Son and carried him to a nearby hilltop overlooking Shadowmere. And there, he buried him. Into the fresh dirt, he drove a sign and then walked away into the setting sun.

Once his figure disappeared over the hills, the storekeeper's wife ran forward to see the name of the mysterious stranger who sacrificed his life for their own.

But there was found no name. Instead carved into the sign was, "MY SON SHALL RETURN. KEEP WATCH ON THE THIRD DAY."

For the next three days, the townspeople discussed and pondered what the sign meant. Surely, it could not mean the Father's dead Son would return. Indeed, he had saved them from the serpent's venom, but he had paid for it with his life. No doubt he would remain where he was buried.

However, on the morning of the third day, all the townspeople found one reason or another to remain nearby the gravesite. Some said they were on a picnic; others said they were out for a stroll while still others said they came to swap horses. No matter their reason, each person kept one eye on their business and another vigilant eye on the grave.

All of a sudden, a rumbling sound was heard in the valley below. The ground began to roll and shake under their feet. Flocks of birds flew into the air as every tree bowed low their thick trunks toward the Son's grave. Some of the townspeople began to flee in terror while others stood fast and remained fixated on the grave. The earth mound on the hilltop began to heave up and down as if some invisible force was pushing up from the deep.

On the third movement upward, the grave split. Out of the ground burst a ray of light that pierced the sky and momentarily blinded the onlooking townspeople. They rubbed their eyes and looked up just in time to see the figure of a man step out of the grave. Clothed in sunshine, he turned and began to walk toward them. Huddling together, too paralyzed to move, they waited for the blazing figure to reach them.

As he drew nearer, the light began to dim, and there was no question as to who stood before them. The blood-stained thread with the serpent's fangs dangled from the Son's neck. But there was something else— something shiny. Upon his chest, a large, silver star that hadn't been there before was pinned. Engraved on the star were the words, "MARSHAL OVER ALL."

"Do not be afraid," the figure spoke to them in a reassuring voice. "I wish you no harm."

"Who...who are you?" someone stammered.

"You know who I am," the Son said.

"But...but we saw you die. How can you now be standing here before us?" a voice cried out from the back.

"Indeed, the venomous sting of death did its best to push me down, but I pushed back. My push was stronger," the Son replied.

"How is that possible? Where did you come from?" another voice asked.

"I am from before all things, so all things are possible."

Some within the crowd exchanged skeptical glances. A well-dressed man brushed dirt from his knees and struggled to smooth out his normally well-groomed hair. He was the town banker, the first to be bitten.

"What about that black serpent?" he asked, "Never seen a serpent act like that. Where'd it come from?"

"Its origin is less important for you to know than its nature. It is a rebel that knows only death, destruction, and disorder. It also hates you with a hatred you cannot begin to fathom."

"Why? What did we ever do to it?"

"You are alive. And as long as you are alive, your destiny as sons and daughters is secure."

"What's our destiny?"

"To rule by my law."

"Your law?"

"Yes, my law."

"Oh—and just how do you figure we do that?" the town banker questioned further, not sure he liked where the conversation was going.

"You must live under my law," the Marshal answered.

Upon hearing this, many within the crowd began to murmur. Personal freedom and very little crime had long been their town's greatest pride. From the back, another well-groomed man pushed his way through the crowd toward the front.

"Excuse me, uh, Marshal. I'm the duly elected mayor of this town and...er, it's not that we don't appreciate what you did for us... it's just that we don't need a Marshal. Never had one. Aren't asking for one. Don't want one."

"Nonetheless, you need me and the authority of my law," the Marshal calmly replied.

The mayor stiffened his posture and cleared his throat. "Well, as I said, we just aren't interested in your... uh, services at this time. We have sort of a 'live and let live' policy around here."

"That won't be enough to protect you from the serpent. It comes to steal, kill, and destroy all that live."

"Why should we fear the serpent?" a voice near the mayor objected. "It ain't here no more."

The Marshal looked over at the town storekeeper who voiced the objection. Soberly, he fingered the fangs around his neck. "The serpent will return. You have not seen the last of it. Its fangs have been broken and its venom has been expended, but it is still dangerous."

"Then what do you propose we do? Run and hide?"

"No, you must fight! You must learn to resist and live in the authority I have won for you."

The storekeeper scoffed, "Nonsense! We are just simple townsfolk. There ain't more than a few guns between us, and most of them are old hunting rifles."

The Marshal took a deep breath. "The battle you must fight against the serpent is not fought by guns and bullets. It is fought with this." He brought his hand up and tapped the shiny badge pinned to his chest. "The decisive victory over the serpent has already been won by me, but you must enforce that victory in your own lives and the lives of your families."

At this, a mother approached. Her baby rested fast asleep on her hip. She placed her hand upon the Marshal's arm. "Kind sir, can you not stay here and help us?"

The Marshal reached over and caressed the back of her sleeping child. "I will help you. But I cannot stay long with you. However, I will never leave you."

Unsure of how that made sense, some began to mock. "Maybe he's a bit daft in the head," one snickered. "Yes, being under the ground so long can't be good for your health," another sneered.

Ignoring them, the town blacksmith, his face and hands blackened with soot, stepped forward. "How do we enforce your victory, Marshal?"

"You must become my deputies. You must swear allegiance to my law and authority and root out every hiding place where the serpent can find safety and shelter."

At this, the former murmuring and mocking began to turn into a loud grumble and complaint. "I don't have time for that! I have a business to run," the storekeeper protested.

"Neither do I," agreed another. "I have my cows and horses to think of. I can't afford to be anyone's deputy."

"Right! I say we just live our lives and forget about that silly snake," the mayor said confidently. "Besides we gave it a lickin' it won't soon forget. It'll be too afraid of us to return."

Others nodded their heads in silent approval and began to reconsider the prior events. The mayor and storekeeper huddled together with the banker and quietly conversed. "Listen, I've been doing some thinking," the mayor began. "Wasn't it *really us* who defeated that foul serpent? After all, we all saw this unknown stranger succumb to his wounds. But not us—*we survived*. We're still a'standing!"

"Right!" the banker swiftly acknowledged. "And that proves we are strong enough on our own *without* this uppity Marshal. Just who does he think he is coming into our town uninvited and ordering us to live under his law?"

"But we saw him come back to life!" someone interjected.

"Did he? We don't know that for sure. It goes against all natural law!" the banker shot back.

"Exactly," the storekeeper nodded. "It ain't natural. Maybe he never *really* died. Or maybe he and the serpent are in cahoots to trick us all—to give up our freedom?"

"Well boys, I think I've heard enough," the mayor spoke up. "You can do what you want, but I've got too many unanswered questions to trade in my freedom for some outsider's laws."

Many within the crowd shared similar thoughts. Some spoke them out loud and others kept them private. The Marshal said nothing in response. He simply waited patiently as different people voiced their opinions and disagreements.

Finally, the mayor, the banker, and the storekeeper broke away and began to walk back to town. A large group soon followed behind. In the end, only twelve remained.

Chapter 3

With great sadness the Marshal watched the majority of the town depart and trudge down the hill. "Many are called, but few seek to be chosen," he sighed aloud before turning to look upon the small group that remained with him on the hilltop.

"You have each made the choice to step into a calling few are willing to accept," he began. "For this, you shall be greatly rewarded. But know the life of a deputy is not easy. Yet it will always be worth it in the end. The day will come when each of you will receive more than you could ever lose in this world."

At that very moment, something very unexpected happened. A majestic, white Dove landed upon the Marshal's shoulder—its feathers tipped in gold. The Marshal cupped his hands over the badge on his chest and breathed over it. As he did this, the Dove upon his shoulder began to flap its wings, slowly at first and then quite vigorously. Immediately, the badge began to glow white hot. When he brought his hands down, badges appeared that looked just like his— though smaller in size. Upon each were engraved the words, **"Deputy of the Marshal."** One by one, he pinned the badges to their chest and saluted them.

The blacksmith, being one of those who remained, stepped forward to ask a question, "Marshal, you mentioned the serpent would return to our town and was still dangerous. Can I ask you to please explain more?"

The Marshal smiled. "Indeed. It is wise to always ask. Those who ask and seek will find—*and be found*. Let me explain what you need to know at this point. The rebel serpent loves darkness and shadows. It hates the light. Not only does it find sanctuary in darkness, it feeds off darkness— especially when it can find such shadows within the souls of people. The serpent can smell such darkness from miles away and will come looking to feed. This is why you must remain in the light. You must never tolerate darkness in your life. You must root it out wherever you find it."

The wife of the blacksmith looked up and saw the sun shining without a cloud in the sky, "But sir, it is always sunny in our town and only dark at night. Are you suggesting we light candles at night?"

The Marshal could not help but smile. "No, my lady. I am not talking about light and darkness as you are used to understanding them. That is why I spoke about the shadows and darkness of the soul. Yes, there will be times when you will need to physically trim the tall weeds around your town where the serpent can nest safely in darkness. But there exists an even greater and thicker darkness that you must be aware of— the serpent's lies."

"Its lies? But the serpent can't talk, can it?" a young lad asked, perplexed.

"Yes, it can. But to you it will only sound like a whisper in the wind. So quiet and crafty are its whispered lies, they can slip through your ears with hardly a sound and make you think they came from your own mind," the Marshal explained before continuing. "In time, you will begin to think you are right to hold such thoughts and attack anyone who tells you otherwise. This is a sign the nature of the serpent is growing within you."

"Is there no defense?"

"Truth is both your defense and your offense. This is why you must allow others to help you examine your heart to discover and root out every poisonous lie that has been planted in your soul by the serpent. Its lies are like poisonous eggs and if they reach maturity and hatch, they will bring ruin upon you."

"Like poisonous eggs? But I thought you said all its poisonous venom was gone?" the young lad asked again.

"Indeed, that is true in part." The Marshal reached up and gripped the serpent's fangs with his right hand. "My Father judged it, broke off its fangs, and together we have taken away its venom. Its bite now can only bruise you, but it cannot kill you."

"But you were bitten, and we saw you die! We saw the serpent kill you," one protested.

"Yes, I did die. But that was not my defeat. That was my victory. I entered the grave to defeat the grave. In this way, I sentenced death to death. All who wear my badge now share in my victory over the serpent's venom of death."

An older gentleman standing near the young lad scratched at the stubble of his jaw. "So why not just kill the serpent now and be done with it?" he challenged.

"One day I shall return again and cut off the head of the serpent," the Marshal declared with total confidence. "But for reasons that are too great for you to understand now, my Father and I have decided to allow it limited freedom to slither about this prairie—and part of that reason is so you can be trained and proven worthy to be my deputies. During this time, you will go forth into other towns and deputize other people with the authority I have given you. In this way, the serpent will be put to shame and defeated by the very same men, women, and children whom it has always boasted are weak, feckless, and unworthy of wearing my badge."

A large, unshaved man, teetering back and forth, hesitantly stepped forward. "But what if'n we are unworthy...what then? I'm just a'nobody and a'nothin. Everybody here knows that... I reckon that serpent ain't got nothin' to be afraid of from the likes of me."

The Marshal looked over at the town drunk swaying unsteady on his feet. His protruding belly had stretched his belt to its last hole; the buckle strained to hold it all together. A hardness around his eyes and mouth showed life had not been kind to him.

"You are right to know the serpent is not afraid of you," the Marshal said. "But it is afraid of me and my light. And as long as you wear my badge, you too are a carrier of my light and authority."

"But if'n you knew who I am... what I've done...you wouldn't really want me, Marshal. I can't do nothin' right..." the man's voice trailed off. Shoulders slumped forward, head down, he began to plod down the hill.

"WAIT!" the Marshal's voice thundered.

Startled, the man stopped in his tracks, too afraid to move a muscle. He heard the footfalls of the Marshal's feet come up behind him. He stiffened his shoulders and closed his eyes for the tongue lashing that he knew was coming.

The Marshal clasped both hands upon the drunkard's shoulders in a firm grip and turned him around. Toe to toe they stood. The Marshal could smell the beer and stale sweat coming from his pores. Everyone took a safe step backwards—certain they were about to witness how the Marshal enforced his law on the unruly and ill-mannered.

"Look into my eyes," came the command.

The town drunk shifted his feet uncomfortably, too afraid and too ashamed to look up.

"Look into my eyes," the Marshal repeated.

The man tried to lift his head, but it felt as heavy as a sack of hammers. He began to whimper. "I... I can't, Marshal. I told you I'm no good... just let me go," he blubbered.

"What are you afraid you will see in my eyes?"

Immediately, the man cried out, "Disappointment! Shame! Condemnation!"

At this, the Marshal's face softened. "Come close, everyone, and stand watch with your brother. A poisoned egg, a whispered lie implanted long ago, is now trying to hatch."

The blacksmith and his wife reached over and took hold of the man's grimy hands. "What can be done for him?" they asked.

"We must speak truth to all that is false," the Marshal replied. "All of you listen closely. What I tell you is of the upmost importance. The deadliest poison the serpent ever possessed was the poison of accusation and condemnation. But my Father squeezed out all that venom too. Once it flowed into me, it was stripped of its power. Because I am pure life and pure good, I gave it no place to accuse me and no place to condemn me. In me, the venom of condemnation was itself exposed and condemned. Now all who wear my badge wear my acceptance."

The Marshal tapped the badge pinned to the front of the man's stained shirt. "Do you know what that means, my friend?"

The man struggled to find the words, then blurted out, "That I ain't no worthless failure!"

"Exactly!" the Marshal replied happily. "But it means even more than that. It means you are loved, forgiven, and clean. I do not love you because you have earned it. I love you because I say you are worth it; and what I say, no one can take away. The badge you now wear testifies that you belong to me. You must never remove it. Now try again to look into my eyes and tell me what you see."

This time the man found it a great deal easier to lift his head. The Dove, still perched upon the Marshal's shoulder, again began to flap its gold-tipped wings, creating a gentle breeze. Immediately, his thoughts began to clear as if a misty, dark fog that had long ago settled on his mind was now being blown away. He stared deep into the eyes of the Marshal. A smile crept into the corners of his mouth and then exploded into a wide grin. "I see! I see! Well, I'll be darned...Wow!" A deep laugh of joy rumbled through his belly.

"Well, go on! Tell us what you see!" someone bellowed.

"I see us fishin'!" he exclaimed excitedly. "We's at my secret catfish hole! Just the two of us—me and the Marshal. And we's havin' a good ole time! I can see it plain as day. We's friends... we's good friends."

Everybody laughed and breathed a sigh of relief. The Marshal gave the man's shoulder a final, reassuring squeeze and then turned to face a woman tugging on his arm. It was the wife of the storekeeper who had been among the first to leave the hilltop. "Dear sir, how can we know if the whispered lies of the serpent are growing inside of us?"

"To the degree you examine your heart and allow others to help you see areas of darkness you cannot see, you are living in the light of truth, and the serpent cannot overcome you with its lies. There is more to say and much you still need to learn, but what I have told you is sufficient for what you need to know at this stage in your journey."

The townspeople nodded their heads, understanding more than they did before but still full of questions. Seeing their continued confusion, he added, "Do not let what you don't know stop you from living out what you do know. What I have revealed to you at this point is enough to make you wise without overwhelming you. You must trust that further understanding and truth will come to you as you need it."

"What happens if we are unfaithful to live out what we know to be true? What if we reject the truth of your law and choose to believe the serpent's lies?" a voice asked from the back.

"Then you will become prisoners of those very lies—or worse."

"What could be worse?"

"That you become a teacher of lies, enslaving others in ignorance. There will come a future day of reckoning when my light will reveal all secrets, and all that is wrong and unfair will be made right. On that day, those who willfully suppressed my law will receive less mercy than those ignorant of my law. To whom much is given much is required."

"That sounds so heavy. Does it have to be so hard?"

"To be a deputy of my authority is a great honor. And to those who steward it well, more will be given." The Marshal paused before continuing. "There is always grace and forgiveness to those who lose their way but later return to the light. But to those who are careless and cowardly and refuse to turn away from darkness, even what authority and light they once had will be lost and forgotten.

Suddenly a small hand shot up into the air. It belonged to a young child, a girl no older than nine. "Sir, what happens if I am afraid...too afraid to be a good deputy? I don't want to be a coward; I don't want to run away, but I don't think I am brave at all."

The Marshal bent down to meet the girl's eyes. "My child, I think you are very brave. You are standing here when many chose to walk away, are you not?"

The girl looked around and nodded.

"Well, I think that was a very courageous decision. I am very proud of you."

The young girl bit her lip, wanting to say more but not sure how. Suddenly, she blurted out, "But, sir, there are still so many things I am afraid of."

The Marshal was silent for a moment. Then he reached down, plucked a small, purple flower from the ground and gently tucked it behind her ear. "Your name is Violet, yes?"

The girl looked up, surprised. "Yes, sir."

"And your father gave you that name because those were the flowers he picked every day to win your mother's heart, correct?"

Behind Violet a small gasp was heard. A woman with sweat stains on her dress, barely hiding her calloused knees, stood off to the side. A quivering hand was cupped over her mouth.

Violet glanced over her shoulder at her mother. Eyes of motherly kindness and sorrow stared back at her. Violet turned back to face the Marshal. "Yes, sir," she answered. "But... my father he died last year from the fever."

Small tears began to form in the corners of her eyes. With the end of his sleeve, the Marshal dabbed her wet cheeks. "Yes, I know, my child. And that has made the world a much bigger and scarier place, hasn't it?"

Sniffling back her tears, Violet nodded her head.

"Would you like to tell me about some of those other things you're afraid of?"

"But, sir... there are so many!"

"Oh, like what?"

"Almost everything! Thunderstorms, dogs, and slugs... and the squeaky door in our barn! But most of all spiders! I am so terribly afraid of spiders!"

A great, hearty laugh burst forth from the townspeople, including the Marshal.

"Oh dear," he said, smiling. "To tell you the truth, spiders aren't my favorite creature, but they do serve an important purpose," he winked. "Is there anything else?"

Violet looked down at the ground and nervously chewed on her lower lip for a few seconds, then shook her head. The Marshal lifted her chin back up and looked into her eyes. "I think there is one more thing you aren't telling me. Don't be afraid, my child. Let it out."

After a small pause, Violet cried out, "The serpent! I am afraid of being bitten! I am afraid of dying. I saw you die. I don't want to die!"

The townspeople suddenly became quiet. It was clear death was still a concern many of them had. The Marshal held out his arms to Violet, and she quickly jumped into them. In his arms, she felt utterly safe. Something about them reminded her of the strong tree limbs she loved to climb behind her barn.

He brushed a wisp of hair from her face and said, "My child, I promise you there is one thing you never have to fear again, and that is death." He then pointed over to a large boulder that long ago tumbled down from a mountain ledge and settled into the valley below. "Do you see that big boulder over there?"

Violet nodded yes.

"If you were standing in the way of that boulder when it crashed into this valley, could it have hurt you?

"Oh yes, sir. It could have killed me!"

"Indeed, it could have. But now look beside it. Do you see its big shadow?"

Again, she nodded.

"Can the big shadow of that boulder hurt you?"

Violet thought for a second and shook her head no.

"Why not?" the Marshal asked.

"Because it's just a shadow. It's just a big, black nothing."

"Exactly! Now I want you to imagine that big boulder represents death. When I died, I died for you, Violet. And because I allowed the boulder of death to already roll over me, it can never roll over you. Instead, only the shadow of death can roll over you. And though shadows can be dark and scary—they cannot hurt you, can they?"

Violet shook her head again.

"That's right! So, when the day comes that you pass through the shadow of death, you don't need to be afraid because I will be with you. We will go through the shadow *together*. We will walk through the "big, black nothing" hand in hand. That doesn't sound so scary now, does it?" he asked.

Violet beamed a wide smile, "That doesn't sound scary at all!"

"Good!" He placed her down next to her mother and looked out over the small crowd before him.

"I must soon leave you, but I will return. Some of you will be returning to family and friends who will treat you as an enemy because you dare to offend them with the truth. It will not be easy. But do not fear or flinch in the face of any hostility. Love large. Forgive quickly, and be generous to all. Whatever you do, never remove my badge. It is the only light the serpent fears, for it alone foretells its coming doom."

The blacksmith again stepped forward, his right hand was balled into a fist, his left clenched a hammer. "Before he left us you told our mayor we must learn to fight off the serpent when it returns. What did you mean by that?"

"Hammer, sickle, sword, and gun cannot injure the dark serpent's thick hide or its devious lies. You must fight by resisting it with this," the Marshal replied tapping his badge, and then pointing at theirs. "You must stand your ground, face it, and never turn your back on it. The badge you wear dispels darkness. Always wear it in the front. One of you shines bright. Two of you are brighter. And three of you are brighter still. Band together. Voice out loud what I have taught you. Whatever shadow the serpent is hiding in will shrink; whatever it latches its jaws onto, it will eventually drop."

"Why?"

"Because you have power to persevere in the light of truth. The serpent does not. Long ago it rebelled against heaven's light. So now it cannot long endure it."

"Does the glow of your badge burn its black hide?" the blacksmith pressed further.

"In a way, yes," the Marshal answered. "Just as black mold cannot abide long in the light of day, so also the serpent cannot abide long in the light of my truth. That is why you must commit yourself to remaining in my light longer than the serpent commits to resisting it. Only then will it flee."

"What if we can't?"

"You must."

"Will we win in the end?"

"Yes."

"How can you be sure?"

"Does the darkness of night fight the morning sun for who will rule the day? Not at all. When the sun rises, the darkness has no choice but to surrender to the day. In the same way, the serpent's lies are no match for my light," the Marshal answered.

Suddenly, a distant cry of pain echoed through the hills, coming from the town. Then another shout for help pierced the air. "You must go now. You are needed. But remember you are not alone. I am with you to the very end."

With great pride, the Son—THE MARSHAL OVER ALL—watched his twelve deputies march down the hill. Hand in hand they walked. He knew there was no bluff in them. Their resolve would put the serpentine *nachash* on the defensive wherever it went. What was done could not be undone. News of the serpent's defeat by the Ancients would spread. Others would join the fight. The tide of battle was about to turn.

Overhead, a white Dove flew.

The End

PART 1 COMMENTARY:
EXAMINING THE CALL TO DISCIPLESHIP AS SPIRITUAL WARFARE

Introduction

Thank you for reading *The Fall and Redemption of Shadowmere*. This little book is really two books in one. The first half is for young readers and adult readers alike. This second half may appeal more to mature readers with more life experience. That being said, young people today are exposed to the harsh realities of spiritual warfare and a morally fractured world much earlier than the generation of their parents. Therefore, I would encourage every reader to read as much as they can, but don't feel any shame if the content proves to be too difficult.

My motivation to begin this book with an allegorical parable goes beyond a desire to simply tell a good story. The goal of every allegory or parable is to help the reader connect to an understanding of human experience that is not based in story—but in reality. The parable story you have just read was meant to reveal two fundamental truths that are connected to the believer's life:

1) The meaning of discipleship
2) Christ's victory over sin, Satan, and death.

Today, many Christians have settled into an overly safe and sheltered idea of what it means to be a disciple of Jesus Christ. For them, discipleship has been reduced to little more than listening to an occasional sermon, staying off drugs, and praying over their meals. The truth is far greater. To be a disciple of Jesus Christ is to "discipline" your life for spiritual war.

Whether you like it, want it, or understand it, your commitment to follow Christ exists on a battleground—not a playground. For you have been born again into a war—a raging, cosmic conflict between good and evil that has been going on long before you were born and may well continue long after you are dead. This war cannot be fought with crusader swords or conquistador spears. Such violence is blasphemous for anyone who professes to follow the One who laid down His life for His enemies.

Long ago, the apostle Paul said, "For we do not wrestle against flesh and blood, but against the rulers, against the authorities, against the cosmic powers over this present darkness, **against the spiritual forces of evil in the heavenly places**" (Ephesians 6:12).

The first thing we must understand as we engage in this cosmic struggle is that there is no neutral ground. There is no "spiritual Switzerland." History is littered with the spiritual corpses of men and women who thought they could ignore this war or play possum.

Don't even try.

Your enemies—"the cosmic powers... the spiritual forces of evil in the heavenly places"—hate you, despise

37

you, and want nothing more than to devour your spiritual potential. They fear what you can become through Christ who strengthens you.

Our true pledge of allegiance and the call to participate in God's "kingdom come"

Your journey as a Christian begins with a pledge of allegiance—not to your national flag but to your Commander-in-Chief—the Lord Jesus. This is the fundamental meaning and essence of baptism. Believer's baptism is a pledge of allegiance that says, "I am rejecting neutrality! I am picking a side. I am on God's side!" To be baptized, then, is to declare war on hostile, cosmic powers—to commit oneself to wrestling "against the spiritual forces of evil in the heavenly places."

We have so many spiritual casualties in our Christian communities because we don't teach this truth enough. Both young and old fail to recognize our lives are lived out on a spiritual battleground.

The good news is that Christ has already won the ultimate victory for us! In that sense, we are not fighting for victory as much as we are fighting from a place of victory. Christ has already secured our world for the day of new creation. And into the ground of His own resurrection He has planted the flag of His eventual return. All that is wrong with the world will one day be made right. Every act of injustice will be overruled by His justice. All sorrow will cease. Every tear will be wiped away.

But the in-breaking of new creation (the kingdom of God) is not accomplished independent of us—*but through us.* We are called to participate—*now*—in Christ's victory. We are called to enforce His victory in our world by becoming disciples of His light, truth, and authority.

That is why the parable story you just read used the illustration of "deputies." In the Wild West years of the American frontier, if a town marshal needed assistance to deal with outlaws, he could deputize normal townspeople to be extensions of his own authority. A deputized townsperson could make arrests and carry out the duties of the marshal because he had been granted authority by the marshal to enforce the law of the land. This really gets to the heart of discipleship.

To be a disciple of Christ is to be a "deputy" of Christ's authority and enforce His victory over darkness in our own lives, and in the lives of those around us. This is all connected to the spread of God's kingdom "on earth as it is in heaven" (Matthew 6:10).

Coming to Christ is the beginning, but *becoming* Christlike is the inner journey

Many Christians rightly understand they are called to "seek first the kingdom of God" (Matthew 6:33), but they fail to understand how to advance the kingdom of God in their own lives. The simple truth is, we can only "seek first the kingdom of God" to the degree we are enforcing Christ's light and truth in our lives first.

"I am the light of the world," Jesus declared. "Whoever follows Me will never walk in darkness, but will have the light of life" (John 8:12). John the disciple would later confirm Christ's words, saying, "If we say, 'We have fellowship with Him,' yet we walk in darkness, we are lying and are not practicing the truth. But if we walk in the light as He Himself is in the light, we have fellowship with one another, and the blood of Jesus His Son cleanses us from all sin" (1 John 1:6–7).

Here John connects walking in fellowship with God and walking in the light with walking in fellowship with "one another." Walking in the light is no private affair. It is a corporate affair—which means it is to be done in fellowship and in community with others (i.e. the church). This in turn brings us into union with the Son of God who "cleanses us from all sin."

To walk in the light, instead of stepping in and out of the light, is to commit oneself to the inner journey of transformation. Transformation is about living from the inside to the outside. But such transformation cannot happen if we are still clinging to the world—grasping for purpose, meaning, and identity from a world that is passing away.

That is why Paul warned us, "Do not be conformed to this world, but be transformed by the renewal of your mind" (Romans 12:2). In many ways, seeking first the kingdom of God begins when we refuse to enter into agreement with the false "truth-claims" of a fallen world that is hostile to the way, the truth, and the life. "Don't you know that friendship with the world is hostility towards God," is how James put it (James 4:4).

When the false values and idols of this world lose their ability to define our worship, then God can begin to define our true humanity. To be human is to be an imager of God. And to be an imager of God is to graft our lives to His values. When we cease trying to nourish our self-worth with the image of the world, we create the internal space necessary for the transformative character and mind of Christ to be formed within us. All things become new. We are born again.

To put it all into modern day English, the Son of God becomes the "password" to our "login" in discovering life itself.

The war is won, but there will be no ceasefire until Christ returns

While it is true Christ has won the war, there are still battles to be won to enforce His victory in our individual lives. The Bible does not warn us about the possibility of "falling away" for no reason (i.e. 2 Thessalonians 2:3). The danger is real. The enemy will seek to dislodge us from our faith if he can.

In recognition of an ongoing spiritual threat, Peter warns us, "So prepare your minds for action, and exercise self-control" (1 Peter 1:13 NLT). And again, he repeats, "Be sober-minded; be watchful. Your adversary the devil prowls around like a roaring lion, seeking someone to devour" (1 Peter 5:8).

To fail to see that our lives overlap an unseen realm of cosmic war, is to make ourselves vulnerable to the enemy's lies and be drawn away from the victorious "high ground" God has secured for us.

As in any war, not getting personally captured by the enemy is soldier training 101. Satan is no fool. He knows he cannot win a war he has already lost. His aim, now, is to take as many people as he can into defeat with him. His rejection of a "ceasefire" is motivated by pure spite. He remains on the prowl for POW's (prisoners of war).

What this means is your hang-ups are not what they seem. Many of our "problems" are symptoms of a wayward soul that is entering into agreement with destructive forces.

This includes your:

Reoccurring temper
Verbal abuse of your spouse
Porn problem
Unrepentant greed
Love of money
Overindulgence in alcohol
Emotional eating and food addiction
Unwillingness to forgive those who offend you
Self-chosen alienation from the body of Christ
Self-righteous legalism
Self-pity parties
Self-loathing

Agreement with fear and worry
Nurturing anxiety with ingratitude
Refusal to have a mindset of thankfulness
Cynical unbelief
Double-mindedness
Cowardice
Fear of man
Addiction to social media
Craving to be affirmed and celebrated by the world
Zealous pursuit of self-promotion
Envy, jealousy, and comparison
Habitual gossip, etc.

We must cease thinking the issues above are only issues of personality and temperament. We must see them as spiritually toxic tactics of the enemy designed to take us out of the fight. Am I exaggerating the threat for effect? Not in the least.

James declared that something so small as the human tongue can "set the course of life on fire" and be "set on fire by hell" when it becomes a tool for filthy, polluting language (James 3:6). If a human tongue can be co-opted by the enemy's domain, leading to our destruction, then how much more can a heart set on rebelling against God's created order bring the totality of our lives into spiritual ruin?

Truth be told, Satan *does not need much*. All Satan needs is a "foothold" to gain entrance into our lives. We are warned, "Don't let the sun go down on your anger and do not give the devil a foothold" (Ephesians 4:27). The satanic realm is very adept at using whatever

43

footholds they are given to destroy marriages, corrupt governments, sow division, breed racial tension—and make our lives a wasteland that does not bear eternal fruit.

A sign of the times: Lovers of self

Paul warned us that in the last days many people will be in "the Devil's trap, having been captured by him to do his will" (2 Timothy 2:26). Was Paul thinking of gross sins like murder, burglary, and rape? Was he envisioning vast numbers of people becoming sex traffickers and porn peddlers? No, for he goes on to list behaviors that are now endemic in our world—if not celebrated and daily endorsed by today's "selfie generation" and entertainment industry.

> "But understand this, that in the last days there will come times of difficulty. For people will be **lovers of self,** lovers of money, proud, arrogant, abusive, disobedient to their parents, ungrateful, unholy, heartless, unappeasable, slanderous, **without self-control,** brutal, not loving good, treacherous, reckless, swollen with conceit, **lovers of pleasure rather than lovers of God**..." (2 Timothy 3:1-4).

Lest we think Paul had in view atheists from an anti-religious establishment, he says the exact opposite in the next verse. They will be "holding to a form of godliness, but denying its power" (vs. 5). In other words, it will be religious form without substance because their *outward* devotion to God will be denied by their *inward* failure to live a transformed life. Their love of self will eclipse their professed love of God.

All of this is the enemy's work.

Becoming "true to self": A re-worked philosophy for meaning without an anchor

We have now entered a "Christian" age where the cardinal virtues are to be "true to yourself," "fulfill one's desires," and "live authentically." That sounds so right—almost pious. But like most philosophies, they aren't tethered or anchored into anything absolute, permanent or fixed. Rather than functioning like a secure lighthouse, guiding our lives to safe harbor, they leave us floating aimlessly—paddling after shifting currents instead of an unmoving shoreline.

Obviously, we don't want to be hypocrites and pretenders, or live our lives subject to whatever is trending on Instagram. Yet how "authentic" am I to be with my self-fulfilling pursuits? What if "being true to myself" is to be racist, violent, and cruel? After all, aren't our prisons filled with predatory people whose way of life can be defined as self-fulfillment above all else? Of course, we all recognize that certain actions are non-consensual, making them crimes. Yet the point still stands. Criminals don't act *against* their authentic desires, but in pursuit of them.

Moreover, what if the desires of my "authentic self" merge with the consensual, mutual desires of a woman to commit adultery? Is that still, "No harm, no foul?"

45

Having worked in S.E. Asia with orphans and abandoned kids for over 10 years, I can testify of the destructive harm caused by fathers and mothers pursuing self-pleasure over self-denial. *It is generational!*

What about something as small and innocent as being on the receiving end of juicy gossip? Such a desire comes so natural to many Americans that entire magazine industries have formed to feed our insatiable appetite for rumor and gossip.

Let's face it—people don't tend to commit adultery, harbor resentments, gossip or commit fraud by acting *contrary* to their "authentic selves," but in *conformity* with them. And therein is the reason we need a higher court of opinion than "the self" to distinguish between sacred truth and perversions of the truth.

Seeing sacred truth as the "I-beams" of a structured, human society

To call something "sacred" is to recognize that its truth value was conceived in the mind of God. Marriage, family, sex, love, purpose, meaning, morality—these realities of life are all sacred because they share a point of origin that transcends human opinion and invention. If human society was a multi-storied building, these sacred truths would be the I-beams holding the integrity of society together. They are rigid and inflexible for good reason!

It is one thing to shift around the placement of windows, update the furniture, and change the paint color. Such cultural, societal shifts won't threaten the integrity of a structure. But to remove or cut through the I-beams of sacred truth, is to foolishly weaken the entire structure and invite societal collapse.

Given that truth is "sacred" to the degree it reflects God's original design for human flourishing, anything of human opinion or invention that is outside the purview of God's "sacred version," is by definition a "perversion." It doesn't mean filthy, fake or phony. It may well be that to rebel against God's version may feel "freeing," "authentic" and "true to self." The Bible never tries to deny this. Instead it affirms the human heart is full of deceit, and out of it flows all manner of wickedness.

Jesus pulled no punches when He declared, "For from within, out of people's hearts, come evil thoughts, sexual immoralities, thefts, murders, adulteries, greed, evil actions, deceit, promiscuity, stinginess, blasphemy, pride, and foolishness. All of these evil things come from within and defile a person" (Mark 7:21-23).

Millions of young people around the world have been deceived into thinking the human heart is a wellspring of truth—an objective guiding light that will never lead them astray. It is now assumed, without question, that simply to have an innate desire or attraction within your "heart of hearts" is all the *justification* one needs to pursue fulfillment of that desire or attraction. God have mercy.

Does life with Jesus begin with a call to *self-fulfillment* or *self-denial?*

The teachings of Jesus stand in sharp contrast to the false "gospel" of commitment without cost. Jesus knew "true north" is not to be found within the heart's moral compass. In point of fact, knowing the heart is internally defiled and not to be trusted, is the reason Jesus did *not* mark out a life of discipleship with a call to "self-fulfillment." Instead He declared, "Whoever wants to follow Me must...*deny themselves*" (Matthew 16:24).

The fact that so many professing Christians have *inverted* this truth, turning it upside down in order to "have their cake and eat it to," is why we are now reaping a Christian culture too "obese" to run a race that requires endurance from start to finish. We are gorging ourselves on pursuits of the flesh and trying to wash down the compromise with just enough religion to settle the nausea of conviction.

Since the time of Eden, the temptation of Satan, the *nachash* serpent of old, has been for us to be enticed by worldly offers that "look good for food... and [are] a delight to the eye...to be desired to make one wise" but in the end bring ruin (Genesis 3:6).

All of this can be defined in a word—**sin.** We can choose to believe the daily carnage of man's inhumanity to man is a result of misunderstood people whose actions simply need to be properly psychoanalyzed and filed away under a fancy worded classification. Or we can call a spade a spade and call ourselves what the Bible calls us—sinners.

A Savior being sent implies a people in need of being saved

Whether we discern it to be true or not, the fact is that Satan has "weaponized" sin's power against us in more ways than one. The good news is that God sent His Son to do something about it. If sin's condemnation is the "currency" of Satan's dominion, then Jesus came to "bankrupt" his domain.

I have always been struck by the fact that the "…good news of great joy" first proclaimed by angels to frightened shepherds on a Bethlehem hilltop was, "…unto you is born this day… a Savior, who is Christ the Lord" (Luke 2:11).

A Savior? A Lord? That implies our "authentic selves" desperately needed saving, and the One to do it could not be a mere human mortal. These two themes— salvation and Lordship—are at the forefront of the Son of God's mission to secure our planet.

Through His death and resurrection, the power of sin, Satan, and death was broken. We now live on resurrection ground where the old is gone and the new has come. But we must die to our old way of life to become partakers of this new creation. Hearing again the words of Jesus on this matter is where we must begin. "Whoever wants to come with Me *must deny himself and take up his cross*" (Matthew 16:24).

To the degree we are picking up our own cross, dying to a former allegiance to self-rule, is to the degree we are walking in the light and united to Christ's victory on the cross. As mysterious as it may sound, when a true union occurs between (1) **our cross** and (2) **Christ's cross**, sin and death no longer have any ultimate hold on us.

To understand *how* and *why* Christ's death on a wooden beam 2000 years ago separates sinners from their sin, we need to back up and retrace in greater depth sin's emergence into the world at the fall of Adam and Eve. What follows is a theological exploration into the Bible to better understand the cross as God's defeat of sin, Satan, and death.

As was stated in the introduction, I realize this material may be a bit challenging—and not everyone has the desire to take "deep dives" into the Bible. All I can say is the shiniest pearls lie at the bottom, and "snorkeling" on the "surface" of the Bible won't get you to them.

PART 2 COMMENTARY:
EXAMINING CHRIST'S DEATH AS VICTORY OVER SIN AND SATAN

Finding ourselves in Eden

Adam and Eve's decision to partake of the forbidden fruit of the knowledge of good and evil was no innocent mistake made in ignorance. Neither was it a desire to introduce more variety into their diet or increase their vitamin C intake. It was a calculated decision to claim divinity on their own terms—"to be like God" and determine right and wrong for themselves (Genesis 3:5). Our daily newspapers now cover what happens when human beings "get it wrong."

Put simply, the fall of humanity in Eden is the origin point for centuries of human heartache, misery, and tragedy. It is the crack through which greed, pride, murder, corruption, and sexual perversion rushed in and fixed itself upon our world and began to feed off the weaknesses of our fleshly desires like an other-worldly parasite feeding off its host.

In this sense, sin is like spiritual gangrene of the soul and body; it will eventually take our lives. If we ignore Genesis 3, the rest of the Bible, not to mention all of human history, becomes virtually impossible to make sense of and understand.

As hard as it is, we must find ourselves in the sad events of Genesis 3. The sober reality that we are "Adam and Eve" must be recognized and admitted. For is it not true that we too are often drawn away from God's words by our self-centeredness and pride? Is it not true that we too are enticed by the Tempter to live independently of God's rule, will, and authority?

Indeed, human history is one long story of God's human imagers continuing to cast off God's moral authority and define right and wrong for themselves.

Remembering the day One "stronger than the strongman" entered our world

We often want to be the hero of our story. But within the pages of Scripture we discover quite abruptly that we are not. The theme of human failure and sin starts only three chapters into Genesis and then courses its way throughout the Bible like a winding river that often floods its banks. The result is widespread destruction.

The story of humanity is the story of sin eroding our true humanity. Recognizing that we are not the heroes and saviors of our own story *is where the gospel begins!* We are rebels and wretches that needed a true hero, One untouched by sin, to step into our wretchedness and restore us as image bearers of God.

We are given a hint right after the Fall of humanity that such a messianic Hero would come, but the how, when, and why is obscure—almost cryptic. God tells the serpentine *nachash*, "I will put enmity between you and the woman, and between your offspring and her offspring; He shall bruise your head, and you shall bruise His heel" (Genesis 3:15).

The crucifixion was God's plan to deal a death blow to the serpent—the rebel *nachash*. But it had to be veiled on purpose. For as Paul declared, "None of the rulers of this age understood this, for if they had, they would not have crucified the Lord of glory" (1 Corinthians 2:8).

In Paul's theology, the term "rulers and authorities of this age" referred to rebel, angelic beings that defected from God's authority long ago (Ephesians 6:12; Colossians 2:15). In the New Testament, Satan is not only revealed to be part of this cosmic rebellion, he is revealed to be the serpent of old—the *nachash* of Eden (Revelation 12:9, 20:2). His defeat at the pierced hands of the Son of God was the greatest "sneak attack" ever conceived.

Paul specifically points to Christ's death on the cross as the key event in human history when God "...disarmed the rulers and authorities and disgraced them publicly; [and] triumphed over them by Him" (Colossians 2:15).

Indeed, on the cross we are beholding nothing less than the fulfillment of ancient prophecy first declared in Genesis 3:15. We are witnessing the crushing blow upon the serpent's head—the day Christ emptied sin of its power to claim humanity by ransacking Satan's stronghold, plundering his possessions, and delivering all captives under his domain.

Christ referred to this same cosmic plundering of Satan's domain of darkness when He declared:

> "If I drive out demons by the Spirit of God, then the kingdom of God has come to you. How can someone enter a strong man's house and steal his possessions unless he first ties up the strong man? Then he can rob his house" (Matthew 12:28–29).

In Christ's illustration, He understands Satan to be the "strongman" and the "ruler of the demons" (Matthew 12:24). However, Jesus is letting it be known that on the basis of driving out demons, He is revealed as being stronger than the "strongman" who is attempting to protect and safeguard the possessions of his house.

By "house" and "possessions," Christ is referring to Satan's kingdom where men and women were held captive under his domain. How were men brought under Satan's dominion? They were taken captive through the power of sin.

We see the same parable analogy in the gospel of Luke, but the words of Christ are even more forceful. In Luke 11:20–22, Jesus declares:

> "If I drive out demons by the finger of God, then the kingdom of God has come to you. When a

strong man, fully armed, guards his estate, his possessions are secure. But when **one stronger than he** attacks and overpowers him, he takes from him all his weapons he trusted in, and divides up his plunder."

The "strong man" Satan was indeed strong, but speaking of Himself, Jesus said, "...one stronger than he" had come. But Jesus didn't come to earth to play nice. He didn't come into the world as a "hippie" to simply utter pithy sayings about lilies in the valley. He came to ransack the enemy's estate. In fact, it is precisely because Jesus overpowered the "strongman" that we can now live like lilies in the valley without being consumed by anxieties, fears, and vulnerabilities.

Notice the choice words Jesus utters. He says He came to "attack and overpower" the strongman and "take from him all his weapons he trusted in" and "plunder" his "possessions" (Luke 11:20–22). Jesus sounds more like a Viking warrior than the meek and mild shepherd we often picture in our minds. But bringing the fight to Satan is exactly what we needed.

The one-two punch: Sin condemned and captives released

In the secret counsel of the Godhead, it was determined that the Son's death had to coincide with both disarming the powers of darkness and condemning sin. Indeed, to speak of one is to speak of the other. From the beginning, Satan's "weaponization" of sin was aimed at getting us to forfeit our destiny to rule the earth as imagers of God. To this end, Satan sought to use sin to bring us under accusation and condemnation.

It is not without reason the Bible calls Satan "the accuser of our brothers and sisters...who accuses them day and night before our God" (Revelation 12:10). As "slaves of sin" (Romans 6:20), we all were held captive to the enemy's domain in this woeful state.

If God's plan was, as Colossians 1:13–14 states, that we be "...delivered...from the domain of darkness and transferred... to the kingdom of His beloved Son, in whom we have redemption, the forgiveness of sins," then somehow the interlocking law of sin leading to condemnation would have to be broken. How it was broken, without God's justice being compromised in the process, is the genius of Christ's atonement.

Everything revolved around the powers of darkness being enticed and lured onto the scene under the false assumption the Son's death was their victory. That, in turn, required the Son to become vulnerable to the worst of sinful humanity. Put another way, in order to redeem human beings *at* their worst, the Son deliberately submitted Himself to humans *to do* their worst to Him.

The Scriptures declare His death was no accident, but a purposeful plan to be "delivered up... [and] crucified and killed by the hands of lawless men" (Acts 2:23). But these "lawless men" did not act alone. Behind the scenes lurked satanic powers, the "rulers of this age...doomed to pass away" who unknowingly brought about their own demise when they "crucified the Lord of glory" (1 Corinthians 2:6–8).

The realm of darkness could not foresee how a selfless act could be their demise

There is a reason the messianic prophecies about the Messiah's death were cryptic and could only be fully understood in retrospect. They were *intentionally* cryptic. The Son's choice to enter our world as one of us, and then enter into death to defeat death, was part of the hidden wisdom of the Godhead the cosmic powers of this age could never have anticipated.

When Jesus revealed Himself in a dusty corner of Galilee, even the demons were shocked and confused as to His appearing. Matthew 8:29 records when they saw Jesus for the first time, they cried out, "What have you to do with us, O Son of God? Have you come here to torment us before the time?"

The inability of the domain of darkness to make sense of the Son's arrival on earth in human flesh is also testified in John 1:4-5, "In Him was life, and the life was the light of men. And the light shines in the darkness, and **the darkness did not comprehend it**" [NKJV].

Recognizing that Christ came to fight, attack, overpower, plunder, and ultimately defeat the enemy is central to understanding the cross and why Christ came to die. But the manner in which that intention was fulfilled on the cross, the enemy could neither prepare for nor comprehend. Satan understands power, control, intimidation, and oppression. But he doesn't know love or self-sacrifice. So selfless, giving, and loving was the death of Christ for sin that Satan never envisioned that such a sacrificial act could bring about his ultimate undoing. When Jesus knew His death was imminent, He said,

> "Now is the **judgment of this world**. Now the **ruler of this world** will be cast out" (John 12:31). And again, on the eve of His death, He said, "...concerning judgment...the **ruler of this world is judged**" (John 16:11).

All of this tells us that Christ's death secured defeat of the enemy's worldly domain on the basis of judgment. The twist is that sin and Satan, rather than sinners, were judged by God. That in turn, resulted in Satan's claim to hold sinners captive to accusation and condemnation being completely canceled. For if the strength of Satan's grip on sinners depended on sin's power to enslave sinners under condemnation, then the plan of the Trinity was to send the Son to demolish the dark "tri-unity" between sin, sinner, and Satan.

This is a central reason why John stated, "...The Son of God was revealed for this purpose: to **destroy the devil's works**" (1 John 3:8).

We are now entering the realm of what it means to be redeemed, rescued, and ransomed. These are the metaphors the Bible borrows to help us understand that Christ's death *for* sin is our liberation *from* sin. Thus far, we have largely been describing *what* the cross achieved. Now we want to deal with *how* these wonderful mysteries were achieved. *How* exactly did Christ's atoning death accomplish the defeat of sin and Satan and our redemption?

Because sin exposes us to further violation, we need covering—or atonement

In keeping with our "deep dive" illustration, any experienced diver will tell you that every so often you need to pause your descent and "equalize" the pressure in your ears before diving further. If not, your eardrums will rupture. In our own theological descent into the meaning of Christ's atonement, we don't want our minds to "rupture." Therefore, a great place to pause and "equalize" our thinking is found in 2 Corinthians 5:2–5. Paul writes:

> "Indeed, we groan in this body, desiring to put on our dwelling from heaven, since, **when we are clothed, we will not be found naked**. Indeed, we groan while we are in this tent, burdened as we are, because **we do not want to be unclothed but clothed**, so that mortality may be swallowed up by life. And the One who prepared us for this very purpose is God, who gave us the Spirit as a down payment."

Here Paul is comparing the state of his fallen, mortal nature as being "naked" and "unclothed." Despite being fully clothed with physical garments, Paul recognizes

59

that something about our sinful world has caused him to feel uncovered and exposed. Although he believes he has already received a "down payment" on being "clothed", he yearns for the day when he will be fully clothed and "swallowed up by life" in the future resurrection.

With this in mind, we can now introduce the theologically dense word "atonement." Many are unaware that in Hebrew the root meaning of "atonement" actually means "to cover" (*kaphar*). We need atonement—true covering—because of what sin *is* and what sin *does*. Sin is an otherworldly presence not part of God's original creation.

Through the fall of Adam and Eve we are told "sin entered the world...and death through sin" (Romans 5:12). As such, sin removes "pieces" of our original "clothing"—the image of God—and renders us naked and exposed to its own desire to violate us further. We tend to think sin is just "doing wrong." The truth is much more sinister and mysterious than that.

Sin is not just a *verb* of action, but a *noun* of presence and power

In both Hebrew and Greek, the Bible speaks of sin as both a verb (doing wrong) and a noun (an otherworldly power). The first time we come across the word "sin" as a noun in the Bible, its presence and power is symbolized as an external force that desires to gain entrance into our lives.

After Cain became furious and despondent that God received Abel's offering but not his, God declares to Cain,

> "If you do what is right, won't you be accepted? But if you do not do what is right, **sin is crouching at the door. Its desire is for you, but you must rule over it**" (Genesis 4:7).

Failing to do what is right is indeed sin (as a verb). But God's warning to Cain is that his failure to do what is right will in turn make Cain vulnerable to what sin is (as a noun).

Somehow failing to do what is right exposes us to sin's beastly nature. This cause-and-effect relationship tells us that whatever sin is, it cannot be reduced to merely "failing to do what is right." It no doubt includes that, but it is also *more* than that.

Even more striking is how God personifies sin as having a "desire" for Cain's life. Personification is when you attach human characteristics to something that is non-human. Sin is not a person, and yet God's first description of sin tells us sin desires to have us be its own possession. (The same Hebrew word for "desire" was earlier used to describe Eve's "desire" for Adam in Genesis 3:16).

God warns Cain he must rule over sin's desire for him—again indicating that sin is like an otherworldly power that must be brought under subjection.

The implication is not hard to miss; if Cain does not, then he will become exposed to sin's devouring nature. As we all know, Cain did not "rule over" sin's desire for him, and soon after, he murdered his brother. If history tells us anything, it tells us humanity has become progressively ruled *by* sin, instead of ruling *over* sin.

Now fast-forward thousands of years to the New Testament. When the writer of Hebrews says Jesus was "tested in every way as we are, yet without sin" (Hebrews 4:15), it is crucial that we see that testimony within the context of God's first description of sin in Genesis 4:7. Jesus was literally "ruling over" sin—giving sin no entrance into His life. That truth is an important "pearl" we will reexamine later as we continue our "deep dive."

Now that we understand the Bible makes a distinction between sin as a *verb* and sin as a *noun*, we can return to the fall of Adam and Eve and see something important the Bible does not want us to miss.

God loved sinners *before* He sent His Son as an atonement

In an earlier section, it was said that the root meaning of atonement means "to cover" and that sin removes pieces of our original clothing—the image of God. Both of these points can be seen at the fall of Adam and Eve. Strange as it may sound, sin exposed the nakedness of Adam and Eve in a manner that needed to be covered or atoned.

62

But not just anything can be used to cover or atone for sin. Adam and Eve realized early on that life, not leaves, was needed to cover over their exposure due to sin.

Sin is, by nature, anti-life because it relationally severs us from the source of life itself—God. Therefore, only Life can ultimately restore life that has been taken from us. On the cross, Life is being given and Life is being taken. But God isn't doing the taking. God is doing the *giving*.

There should be no doubt about this point.

"For God **so loved** the world," Jesus declared of the Father, "that **He gave** His only Son... that the world might be **saved** through Him" (John 3:16–17).

Though we are undeserving of it, Divine love was the incentivizing motive behind God's decision to send His Son into the world. Paul will later agree, stating, "But **God proves His own love for us** in that while we were still sinners, Christ died for us!" (Romans 5:8)

To the degree sin uncovered us is to the degree Christ came to re-cover us. He came to restore us to our true humanity—which is nothing less than being restored as imagers of God. Only then can we be fully *one* with God again (reconciliation).

Only then can lasting "at-one-ment" (atonement) be accomplished. But all of this required God to deal with our sin on a "once-for-all" basis. All previous dealings with sin were temporary in nature—shadows of the Person that would come and cover us with His own life.

Lots of baggage: Unpacking the wrath of God

Many Christians wrongly assume the message of the cross can be reduced to telling people: *"Your sins made God angry. But the good news is that Jesus absorbed God's anger and wrath against you, so now God's wrath is exhausted and He loves you."* Whether intended or not, this is the unfortunate sound bite quite a few Christians are left with after years of being sermonized.

The result is an unhelpful division that assumes the Father takes on a posture of judicial *payback* on the cross, and the Son takes on a posture of judicial *forgiveness*. This we cannot say. Instead, on the cross, both the Father and the Son are displaying a posture of forgiveness. Indeed, on the cross, the Father's love for the world is *coming into union* with the Son's love for the world—and we are "graced" to get caught in the middle.

At this point, we need to say a few words about what the Bible calls, "God's wrath."

There is so much misunderstanding about God's wrath. When people hear of the wrath of God, they tend to envision everything from an enraged, violent father terrorizing his children to the Incredible Hulk unleashing pent-up fury on hapless people. Let's toss these misconceptions into the wastebasket immediately. God's wrath is not a divine temper tantrum. Nor is

God's wrath the "dark side" of His personality that had to be pacified *before* He could desire to love sinners.

Rather, God's wrath is His morally perfect *response* to everything that opposes the good of His nature. In other words, "God's wrath" is shorthand language for God's righteous and holy opposition to all evil. It is not God getting His "pound of flesh."

If God is good, then it means God's nature stands opposed to everything that is by definition *not* good.

Being made in God's image, we reflect in part God's wrath in our own desires to right the wrongs of this world. When you hear of a child being trafficked for sex, a corrupt judge being bribed, or justice being denied—and something wells up within you, screaming, "That's not right!"—you are experiencing a taste of the morally good wrath of God. It is in your spiritual DNA as a human image-bearer of your Creator!

Now that we understand God's wrath to be His holy and perfect opposition to everything contrary to holiness—i.e., sin—we can better understand what is happening on the cross without getting trapped in misconceived, bad theology that reduces the image of the cross to the Father angrily punishing Jesus to exhaust His fury. Nor are we left floundering on the idea that Christ's physical suffering *causes* God to forgive sinners.

On the contrary, the cross is a manifestation that our God *has always been* a forgiving God, who seeks to act on behalf of sinners with mercy and love while simultaneously maintaining His just opposition against sin. For God cannot just wink at sin and wish it all away willy-nilly. God must deal with sin, and deal with it decisively. But it will come at a cost.

As will be shown by the end, there is a sense in which we can say God's justice was satisfied on the cross, but such satisfaction didn't happen by *extracting payment out of Jesus' sufferings,* as if it was a moral debt that could only be paid *if* Jesus reached some divinely appointed threshold of pain.

Immediate clarity emerges once we stop thinking that the wrath of God was directed **against** Christ. Instead, we need to see how the wrath of God was operating **through** Christ.[1]

Understanding how all this worked is where the atonement comes into sharp focus without us losing sight of love and justice being displayed by both the Father and the Son. Our starting place is realizing the target of God's wrath is sin and Satan's domain—*not the Son.*

What you are about to read involves a theory of Christ's atonement I call the *Perfectus Liberatio* view of the atonement. That is Latin for "Perfect Liberation" because it is only through Christ's sinless perfection that sin itself was condemned and emptied of its power to claim us under its domain.

Indeed, sin's condemnation and our liberation fit together like a hand in a glove. Many of these thoughts will be expanded in a forthcoming book. For now, I only offer a summary.

Turning the tables on sin: Sin's condemnation *of sinners* versus God's condemnation *of sin*

In the divine wisdom and plan of the Godhead, the Son is allowing Himself to become subject to the full measure of evil—in both the earthly realm and the spiritual realm. But in His doing so, the hostile powers of darkness become fully exposed and vulnerable to God's purpose to redeem and rescue us from their dark domain.

Consider the following: If sin gave the powers of darkness the right to hold men and women captive to their domain of accusation, condemnation, and death, then what would happen if the powers of darkness lost "access" to our sins?

More specifically, what would happen if the sin of the world could not only be transferred, but fully absorbed into a Being so righteous and innocent, that the nature of that pure Being stripped sin of its powers of condemnation?

Make no mistake about it—this is exactly what happened on the cross behind the scenes in the unseen, supernatural realm. Instead of sin being able to tempt and condemn its new "host," sin itself becomes exposed to God's righteous condemnation. The result is the total undoing of sin's potency.

As in the parable story you just read, the *defiling* nature of the serpent's venom was undone by the immunity of the Son's blood. Similarly, on the cross sin met its match in the perfection of Christ's sinless nature and was undone. Now all that come through Christ's redeeming blood receive the same "immunity" and pass from death to life.[2]

Just think about it. The power of sin has always been its power to both **defile** and **condemn** its human "hosts" as being "in the wrong" (guilty), and thus worthy of condemnation. Therefore, if sin is to be condemned, sin *itself* must be judged to be "in the wrong" (instead of us)! But how can this be accomplished?

There is only *one* way.

The sin of the world must be absorbed into a Being so righteous and perfect that sin can neither defile, nor condemn the sin-bearer of any wrongdoing—not even an errant thought. Only then can God condemn sin and judge it to be "in the wrong." Because all sinners fall short of the glory of God, God could never judge sin to be "in the wrong" in any of our lives. On the contrary, we have given sin every reason and right to dwell in us!

But Christ is altogether different. He is without sin. Yet, on the cross, He is choosing to take upon Himself the sin of the world. It is here, and only here, where the holy wrath of God and the incarnation of the Son *converge* to accomplish reconciliation for the world.

Given that some of this material may be new to you, it is worth developing more. With the basic structure of God's plan in place, we now need to "furnish" it, and deal with some questions along the way.

A distinction with a difference: God's condemnation of sin—*not the Son*

The Mosaic law served to carve out clear boundary markers to warn people of sin's destructive nature, much like a signpost might warn people against entering a radiation zone. Much of the Old Testament is a record of Israel rebelling against those boundary markers and becoming infected with terminal levels of sin's toxic "radiation." However, a remnant of believers always found refuge in obedience and faithfulness.

In this sense, the Mosaic law preserved Israel long enough until Israel's Messiah came to do what the law could never do—condemn sin itself. Although the law was very good at pointing out human fault and the condemning nature of sin, how does one go about condemning sin *itself*? Such a concept strikes us as utterly mysterious—*if not preposterous.*

And yet this is the central act that is occurring on the cross that allows God to "transfer us out of the domain of darkness into the kingdom of the Son of His love" (Colossians 1:13).

In order for God to redeem sinners from sin's condemning enslavement, sin itself needed to be condemned as being "in the wrong" and sinners needed to be put "in the right." Scripture's announcement that God put us "in the right" (declared righteous) through Christ (Romans 3:26) is not just an abstract theological truth; it is our only means of being liberated from sin's condemnation.

All theories on the atonement have sought to wrestle with this concept. Almost all agree Jesus Christ steps into our place—as a substitute—and accomplishes something for us on the cross. Moreover, they agree God's condemnation of our sin is also occurring on the cross.

But far too often the way this gets expressed is to say the legal *guilt* of our sins was imputed to Christ and therefore God was physically punishing Christ (in our place) to extract payment for offended justice and to appease His anger against sinners. These ideas, as noble as they may be in their intentions, are erroneous. To use a clunky idiom, they "get hold of the wrong end of the stick."

On the cross, God is *not* condemning Christ; God is condemning sin in the humanity *of* Christ. More specifically, God is condemning sin in the righteous humanity of Christ. It may be that you think there is no distinction to be made between saying:

God condemned Christ *for* our sin, or
God condemned sin *in* Christ.

My aim is to help you see that not only does such a distinction exist, but that very distinction is the ground upon which God's victory over sin is anchored.

Paul confirms that sin, *not the Son,* was the target of Divine condemnation

The question now is: Is it scriptural? Is it true that the Father emptied sin of its power by condemning sin in the perfect righteousness of His Son? And is it true the Son came in the likeness of our sinful flesh, but remained sinless and guiltless throughout His earthly sojourn?

Paul clearly thinks so. Listen to how he describes what is occurring in Christ's death in Romans 8:1-4:

"Therefore, **no condemnation now exists for those in Christ Jesus**, because the Spirit's law of life in Christ Jesus has set you free from the law of sin and of death. What the law could not do since it was limited by the flesh, **God did. He condemned sin** in the flesh by sending His own Son in flesh like ours under sin's domain, and as a sin offering, in order that the law's requirement would be accomplished in us who do not walk according to the flesh but according to the Spirit."

These passages are some of the most powerful in the whole Bible. For Paul, they are like the crescendo of a long symphony that has been playing for years and building up to a peak. At the very "top" is a key phrase

71

Paul does not want us to ignore. In verse 3 he says, **"God condemned sin in the flesh..."**

The context of "flesh" represents Christ's humanity on the cross. It is at this point that we must be very careful and listen to Paul's exact words. Paul does *not* say, "God condemned His own Son." He says, "God condemned sin in the flesh... [of] His own Son."

Remember what was stated above. To be condemned is to be examined in the light of God's good wrath and be found "in the wrong." But when Christ absorbed the sin of the world into Himself, sin itself (rather than sinners) became exposed to God's condemnation for the first time. Why? Because sin could not find a justifiable reason to accuse Christ and render Him guilty and worthy of condemnation.

Therefore, Christ's victory over sin is *not* found in Him becoming legally *guilty* and deserving of condemnation. Quite the opposite! It is found in His perfect righteousness offering sin no place to attach itself—no place to condemn Him as guilty. Unable to justify its presence by lobbing an accusation against Christ that would "stick," sin itself is now vulnerable to judgment. Christ's innocence allowed God to condemn sin, instead of sinners, and pave the way forward for us to be forgiven and redeemed of all our sins.

Consider the nature of Velcro. For Velcro to stick, you must have two sides, the hooks and the barbs, for attachment to happen. Like pointlessly trying to stick Velcro to a mirror, Christ is as "smooth as glass"—He offered no "hooks" of sin for the "barbs" of accusation to latch onto. The same cannot be said of us, or any other human being. As the prophet Isaiah also prophesied:

"All we like sheep have gone astray;
we have turned—every one—to his own way;
and the Lord has laid on Him
the iniquity of us all."(Isaiah 53:6)

Having transferred the sin of the world upon His only Son, the Father then canceled every claim sin had upon humanity by "condemning sin" in the perfect righteousness of the Son's sinless humanity. What this means is that sin itself was judged to be in the wrong—*not the Son!*

We are pretty deep in our theological "dive" right now, but don't give up. Exploring is half the fun!

Was God extracting payment from Christ's suffering to get "paid" for our moral debt?

As we alluded to previously, many Christians fail to draw a distinction between Christ's sufferings on the cross *due to sin* from God's condemnation *of sin*. This failure has led some theologians to merge them together and locate God's presence and activity on the cross in a most unhelpful manner. They suggest God is to be found on the cross inflicting punishment on Jesus as a means of extracting payment and satisfaction out of Jesus' sufferings to appease His anger and settle a debt of sin we owed Him.

73

The way this often gets presented is to say, "God can't just forgive or cancel our debt of sin for free. Therefore, God had to inflict punishment on Jesus to pay off His offended justice." However, this is a false assessment. We are being told that **if** (1) we don't believe God was extracting payment for our moral debts out of Jesus' suffering, **then** (2) we must conclude our forgiveness came at no cost.

The conclusion does not follow from the premise.

To connect the Bible's "dots" and be left with this picture staring back at us is most unfortunate. God was not like a divine accountant that successfully shifted payment for sins over into Christ's "ledger" in order to get "what's owed Him."

Moreover, when Paul declared in 1 Corinthians 6:19–20, "You are not your own, for you were bought at a price," Paul does not mean God both *bought* us and *paid Himself* simultaneously. Instead, Paul means God purchased us from sin's domain of death through the giving of His Son. In other words, God is "paying out" not "getting paid."

If the Father "got paid" by Jesus for our transgressions against Him, then it would mean there is no true forgiveness. Rather, there is payment. It is a settlement rather than real grace. Because grace, not settlement, is at the core of the gospel, we should be careful *not* to view the cross as Jesus settling a debt *that the Father was holding onto* and insisting must be paid in the form of inflicted punishment on Jesus.

To assume God is directly inflicting punishment on Jesus, so that His offended justice gets "paid off" by Christ's sufferings, is to collapse the atonement into a theology of being redeemed from *bondage to God* instead of from *bondage to sin*.

This we cannot say.

The reason is quite simple. The purest form of forgiveness is about releasing someone from a debt, not extracting it from the wrongdoer or even someone else before you forgive them. In the two principal parables where Jesus teaches on forgiveness (the prodigal son and the king's servant), we see the forgiver relieving the debt and canceling the wrong by absorbing the loss instead of demanding payment for the sake of offended justice.

Does God absorb the "loss" by getting paid? No—He gives the Son! In that sense, forgiveness for sins "once for all" is certainly not free. It required dual acts of giving. The Father gives the Son and the Son gives His life. Both are *paying*. Neither are *paid*.

When we sing the beautiful hymn, "Jesus Paid It All," there is no need to envision the Father giving Christ up to death, and then circling around to the other side of the cross to get paid. God is not giving with His left hand in order to take with His right hand.

How this mistaken assumption is made is somewhat understandable because we see Christ experiencing great suffering on the cross. Therefore, it is assumed by some that an angry God must be personally inflicting, smiting, and punishing Jesus to acquire judicial payment for our sins.

But this is not the case at all.

Was our redemption dependent on Christ reaching a certain threshold of pain?

Although Christ was definitely experiencing profound pain on the cross, the victorious success of Christ's atonement *for people* was not "hitched" to Christ's nerve endings in order to make it "work." If Christ had suffered one lash stroke more, or one less, or been pricked by one thorn more or one thorn less, or suffered one minute longer or one minute less on the cross—it would not have added to or undermined the atonement one iota.

This is because the redeeming value and power of Christ's atonement was not related to some **threshold** of physical pain He had to endure in order to satisfy His Father's justice—or appease His wrath. If we assume it was, it would *logically* mean *if* Christ had painfully stubbed His toe on the way to Golgotha, it would have accomplished an even *greater* redemption for the world. Do we really want to think this?

The point is, we need to distance ourselves from any theology that would cause us to wonder if an increase or decrease in Christ's physical sufferings would have brought about a corresponding increase or decrease in the "appeasement" value of His atonement.

All this being said, there is a sense in which we can say that Christ is taking our deserved punishment, but the punishment *wasn't* reaching a level of physical pain via crucifixion. Otherwise, we would be forced to assume that the thousands of victims Rome crucified, such as the two thieves being crucified next to Jesus, successfully accomplished their own redemption and "paid for their own sins" in virtue of physically suffering on a cross similar to Jesus.

As will be more fully developed, any theology of substitution and punishment cannot go beyond what Scripture describes as Christ's decision to be our sin-bearer who absorbs into Himself sin's "wages" and enters death on our behalf. But even here, we are not merely referring to the *pain of dying.* The nature of death—as an enemy to be defeated—goes much deeper than the mere physicality of bodily death.

For example, when Jesus declared in John 3:16, "Whoever believes in Me will not perish, but have everlasting life," Jesus was under no delusion that because He physically died that we could *never* physically die. When the Bible speaks of death and perishing, it often does so within a context of the "second death"—an eternal death.

For example, it is exactly *because* Christ knew His church would face persecution unto death (the first death), that He proclaimed, "Be faithful until death, and

77

I will give you the crown of life... The victor will **never be harmed by the second death.** (Revelation 2:10–11).

As such, there is no contradiction in saying Christ sets us free from death, while also recognizing that all of us will physically die. Christ made that abundantly clear when He declared, "I am the resurrection and the life. The one who believes in Me, **even if he dies, will live**" (John 11:25).

Can sin itself be afflicted or condemned with physical punishment?

If our redemption and salvation is *not* to be found in the idea that Christ had to reach a threshold of physical pain to "make it work," where does that leave us? How about sin itself? Was God inflicting physical punishment on sin? This assumption is equally misguided. The reason is obvious. Sin is not a *physical* substance that can suffer physical pain! You can't drive a nail through sin, lash it with a whip, or pierce it with a thorn. Nor can you take it behind the woodshed and spank its backside.

Thus, in order for sin to be condemned by God, it makes no sense to suggest sin needed to suffer retributive punishment through physical suffering. Sin simply can't be punished or condemned in any *physical*, retributive manner.

Interestingly, when the Bible does directly speak of God canceling and forgiving our debt of sin on the cross, it does *not* do so within a context of God inflicting punishment on Jesus to pay off His offended justice. Instead, it ties it into God disarming the spiritual rulers and authorities! If our starting assumption is that rebel, cosmic powers were using our sins to enslave us under their dominion, it all makes sense. Just listen to how Paul unveils what is occurring *behind the scenes* on the cross.

> "And when you were dead in trespasses and in the uncircumcision of your flesh, He made you alive with Him and forgave us all our trespasses. He erased the certificate of debt, with its obligations, that was against us and opposed to us, and has taken it out of the way by nailing it to the cross. He disarmed the rulers and authorities and disgraced them publicly; He triumphed over them by Him." (Colossians 2:13–15)

Given the fact that sin can neither be condemned nor punished through whips, thorns, and nails, we need to look elsewhere for how God brings about our liberation from sin's domain. Key to all this is to recognize that our liberation and forgiveness from sin is not set apart from, but *coinciding* with, sin's condemnation and Satan being disarmed. He was disarmed and plundered of his captives because he lost access to our sins by which to hold us captive to *his own domain of condemnation* leading to death.

With this in place, we can now put the various pieces together to see why Christ's death was both victory over sin and the plundering of Satan's domain. Remember what we set forth early on. Jesus didn't come into our world to play nice. He saw Himself as *stronger* than "the strongman" of Satan, whose domain He had come to plunder (Luke 11:20).

If sin was Satan's domain, then death was his citadel of defense holding us captive. To break us out, a battering ram would be needed. By now I think we can guess what, or should I say *who*, that battering ram was.

Distinguishing between the *penalty of death* and an alleged *payment to God*

None of what has been said so far should be taken to mean Christ is *not* bearing the penalty for our sins. Let there be no doubt about this point. But as it concerns the death of Christ, to speak of *penalty* for sins is different than speaking of *payment* to God. Christ is certainly bearing our sins and iniquities—and therefore the penalty for our sins on the cross. However, we must understand sin's penalty was death—a law of consequence Adam and Eve were forewarned about in Eden. God said, "... the day you eat of it, you will certainly die" (Genesis 2:17).

Paul will later build on this saying, "For the wages of sin is death, but the gift of God is eternal life in Christ Jesus our Lord" (Romans 6:23).

In other words, death is what sin *earns*—not in a divine, revengeful sense—but a consequential sense. The "wages of sin" are the natural and spiritual consequences of rebelling against the Source of life.

Therefore "the wages of sin" are not "wages" God deals out. That is not to say God *hasn't* or *can't* put people to death for their sins. He certainly has and He certainly can. However, that is *not* what is occurring on the cross.

Although the substitutionary nature of Christ's death for our sins should never be questioned, it bears repeating that God is not personally *punishing* Jesus to death "to get paid" or satisfy His justice. Jesus is simply not the object of God's attention *in that way.*

Actually, it is quite the opposite.

On the cross the Father is surrendering His Son over to death, so much so, that the Son feels isolated, abandoned, and forsaken by the Father—not personally afflicted by the Father. Christ's cry, "My God, my God, why have You forsaken Me?" is not due to a *literal* detachment between the Father and the Son (since that would dissolve the triune nature of God). Instead, the "absence" from God that the Son experiences on the cross is an experience within His soul of what sin *is* and what sin *does.*

Remember, sin is anti-life because it is rebellion against the very One who first breathed life into us. Christ's humanity is literally dying because to take on our sin is to literally take on the anti-life properties of sin. Christ's cry is a cry of real death.

Although it was the will of the Father that Christ be "...delivered up [into] the hands of lawless men" (Acts

2:23), to indeed be pierced for our transgressions, we need to see Christ's crucifixion in terms of God *giving up* His Son—not *punishing* His Son. Paul declares that the Father "...did not spare His own Son, but **gave Him up**" (Romans 8:32). And what exactly was the Father giving His Son up to? His own anger? No—the domain of death held by the Devil.

Who was the one "holding the power of death"— Satan or God?

Since the Bible emphasizes there to be a correlation between sin and death, called "the law of sin and death" (Romans 8:2), it is no surprise to see that death is the principle penalty or punishment for sin that Christ suffers as the sin-bearer. But equally important to note is "death" as punishment cannot be removed from Satan's dominion and control—especially as it relates to Christ's death.

When Christ chose to empty Himself and lay down His life as an offering for sin, He was consciously choosing to forfeit life and suffer our deserved penalty in both an earthly and cosmic sense. He was in essence surrendering Himself over to the power and dominion of the enemy—***not the Father***.

But this too was part of the plan of the Divine plan.

If death is the final consequence of sin, then perhaps death is also the answer to sin. There are two kinds of "death." There is death *due to sin*, and then there is death to *deal with sin*.

If sin introduced death to sinners, then perhaps the death of a righteous One can banish the one holding the power of death over sinners—Satan.

This seems to be suggested in Hebrews when the writer declares that the central mission behind Christ's death on the cross was "...that through **His death He might destroy the one holding the power of death— that is, the Devil**—and free those who were held in slavery all their lives by the fear of death" (Hebrews 2:14–15).

Let's be clear about what the Bible is stating. To the degree the devil is declared to be the one "holding the power of death" is to the degree we cannot say that the Father was directly punishing His Son to death. Put simply, the cross is the signature moment in history when the Son surrendered Himself *up to death*, and the Father surrendered His Son *over to death*. Their unified agreement that He would enter death to bury our sins was the key that unlocked our freedom from sin's lawful condemnation.

Christ entered the devil's domain to sentence death to death

Living under sin and Satan's domain of death was the state of a fallen world's hopeless condition prior to Christ. In the weakness of our sinful flesh, the law of sin and death was like a hundred-pound cement block tied to our ankle, dragging us under the water. No matter how good our efforts, no matter how strong we were at swimming, the weight of our sin pulling us under was too much.

Our only hope was God severing the "rope" that connected us to our sin. The link between sin, sinner, and death had to be dealt with once for all—but without the justice of God being compromised.

But how could this be done? Somehow the lawful consequence and curse of sin, death itself, would have to be carried into the grave by a righteous man and be buried on God's terms—*not on sin's terms.*

Sin's terms involved guilt and condemnation holding unrighteous sinners in the grip of "the one holding the power of death—that is, the Devil" (Hebrews 2:14). God's terms involved an act of sacrificial love to enter death and ransack the devil's domain and set us free.

The irony is as profound as it is true. Christ went into the grave to defeat the grave. On the morning of His resurrection, He breaks the bonds of death holding Him. As an eyewitness of this fact, Peter declares, "God raised Him up, ending the pains of death, because it was not possible for Him to be held by it" (Acts 2:24).

Like being swallowed up by a great beast, only to kill it from the inside, so also Christ's aim was to enter the realm of death to defeat it *from the inside.* But He would not go in alone. He would take us with Him and bury our sins there. Together we have died; together we are raised. For this reason, the Bible says, "Now if we died with Christ, we believe that we shall also live with Him, knowing that Christ, having been raised from the dead, dies no more. **Death no longer has dominion over him**" (Romans 6:8–9 NKJV).

It should be obvious by now that when the Bible speaks of death, it is not simply speaking of dirt and holes in the ground. [3] It is referring to a sinister dominion overlapping spiritual powers. That is why we are told, "You have died with Christ, and he has **set you free from the spiritual powers of this world**" (Colossians 2:20 NLT).

Because there is a tendency among some Christians to squeeze the entire saga of the cross into a dense and bitter pill that majors in punishment language and minors in spiritual warfare, we can miss the true nature of the cross as God's triumph over sin.

As the above section highlights, we should only use "punishment" or "chastisement" language (i.e. Isaiah 53) within the context of Jesus' voluntary choice to be in agreement with His Father's will that the wages of sin (the penalty of death) fall on Him, so that the gift of eternal life can fall on us.

To push this further into a theology that insists the Father's wrath was extracting satisfactory payment for sins out of Jesus *in the form of inflicted punishment,* is to turn the atonement on its head! As already stated, it would falsely mean we are being redeemed, rescued, and ransomed *from* God instead of *by* God.

If God's wrath was not inflicting punishment on Jesus, where is it to be found on the cross?

In seeking to correct the error that assumes God's wrath was punishing His Son to death, some theologians swing too far the other way. They assume the wrath of God was nothing more than God giving His Son over to the consequences of our sin—death.

This "overcorrection" is equally problematic. For if the wrath of God was nothing more than the Father allowing the Son to die for our sins, then we are left with the idea that God's wrath is just *watching Jesus die.* But I would argue God's wrath is not passive. It is actively engaging Christ on the cross.

The crux of the issue is now before us.

If God's wrath is not to be found in God extracting payment from Christ's physical suffering, and it means more than passively watching His Son die, where exactly is God's wrath to be found? And how are we to see it? The *Perfectus Liberatio* (Perfect Liberation) view that I am presenting would argue God's wrath is found right where it was needed the most—on the cross, condemning sin and casting out Satan's claims upon a fallen world like a judge throwing out a baseless libel suit with no merit.

Recognizing *where* and *how* God's wrath is being exercised will be explored more fully in our next section as we begin to surface from our "deep dive."

What was sin's "kryptonite"—punishment or perfection?

Here, our starting place is to return to Paul's critical point in Romans 8:3. Paul begins by outlining why the law could not condemn sin. He says the law "could not, since it was limited by the flesh." Other translations say the law was "weakened by the flesh." When Paul speaks of the "flesh," he means human beings—you and me.

His point is that all people have failed to live up to the standard of God's law. Therefore, our universal weakness in keeping the law meant God could not depend upon our moral ability to produce a perfect track record of obedience that would allow God to rescind and condemn sin's claims upon our lives.

But then things get interesting. Paul suddenly pivots and says, "...what the law could not [do]... God did." God did what and through whom? Paul doesn't leave us guessing long. "**He condemned sin** in the flesh," he proclaims, "by sending His own **Son in flesh like ours under sin's domain**, and as a sin offering."

Herein is the necessity of the incarnation—God the Son becoming human. In order for God to "condemn sin in the flesh," God had to send His own Son as a human "in flesh like ours under sin's domain." In putting it this way, Paul is declaring that Christ beat sin on its own turf!

The Son entered sin's domain "in flesh like ours" in order to defeat its domain. Whereas the *moral weakness* of all people brought them under sin's condemnation, the *moral perfection* of the Son would enable God to bring sin under His condemnation. Total reversal!

It cannot be stated enough that the centerpiece of Christ's victory over sin had nothing to do with God reaching a pacified settlement through the means of physical punishment, but had everything to do with Christ becoming the offered up-sin-bearer through whom sin could not lay a charge against!

We have now circled back to our central point. God's prosecution and condemnation of sin did *not* require physical **punishment**. It required moral **perfection**.

This in turn brings God's wrath into proper focus. When we remember God's wrath is not an emotional outburst of anger, but God's morally good response to everything that is not good, we can better see how God's wrath is intersecting with Christ's moral perfection to *condemn sin* and secure our liberation *from sin*.

We can see the drama of the cross unfold within a legal context, but only in the following way. If we adopt the penal/legal metaphor, we can say the Father is the prosecutor. Sin is the defendant on trial. And the courtroom is the perfect righteousness of Jesus. For it is only in the righteousness of Jesus that sin can be put on the defensive. If sin was put on trial in the "courtroom" of another person's life, sin would have every right to be there! And thus, sin would be the *prosecutor* rather than the *defendant*.

But in Christ, all this gets turned around!

For only in the courtroom of Christ's moral perfection could the curse of sin be both fully *absorbed* and fully *condemned* by the Father.

Scripture's remarks on Christ's sinless perfection

Unlike Cain who utterly failed to "rule over" sin's beastly presence "crouching at the door" (Genesis 4:7), Christ fully ruled over sin—and did so without fail. It is no exaggeration to say the Bible wants to emphasize that Jesus went to the cross as a sin*less*, morally perfect person. For example:

> Hebrews 4:15
> "For we do not have a high priest who cannot sympathize with our weaknesses, but One who has been tempted in all things as we are, **yet without sin.**"

> 1 John 3:5
> "You know that He appeared in order to take away sins; and **in Him there is no sin.**"

> 1 Peter 2:22–23
> **"He did not commit sin**, and **no deceit was found in His mouth**; when He was reviled, He did not revile in return; when He was suffering, He did not threaten but entrusted Himself to the One who judges justly."

Hebrews 9:13–14
"For if the blood of goats and bulls and the ashes of a young cow, sprinkling those who are defiled, sanctify for the purification of the flesh, how much more will the blood of the Messiah, who through the eternal Spirit **offered Himself without blemish to God**, cleanse our consciences from dead works to serve the living God?"

1 Peter 1:18-19
"For you know that you were redeemed from your empty way of life inherited from the fathers, not with perishable things like silver or gold, but with the precious blood of Christ, **like that of a lamb without defect or blemish."**

1 Peter 3:18
"For Christ also suffered for sins once for all, **the righteous for the unrighteous**..."

Romans 5:19
"For just as through one man's disobedience the many were made sinners, so also **through the one man's obedience** the many will be **made righteous**."

One of the most powerful and awe-inspiring verses in the Bible is 2 Corinthians 5:21: "He made the One who **did not know sin to be sin for us,** so that we might become the righteousness of God in Him."

Here we are in the realm of mystery meeting majesty. Because sin is not a physical substance you can put in your hand and hit with a hammer, any attempt to "whittle" it down into a theological formula that exhausts all mystery, is misguided. What I believe can be said is as follows. Since sin is not a physical thing that contains mass, to bear our sins had nothing to with the weight of gravity. Rather we are talking about the immeasurable weight of sin's moral impurity, defilement, guilt, and corruption. But Jesus Christ is the sinless, spotless Lamb of God!

"He was revealed so that He might take away sin, and **there is no sin in Him**," is how we saw John summarize this truth (1 John 3:5). What this means is quite astonishing to consider. Once He bore our sins, the sin-*ful*-ness of sinners became undone in the sin-*less*-ness of Christ. Indeed, it was only because the sum of Christ's perfection was greater than the sum of sin, that God was able to condemn sin.

By way of analogy, we can say, what pure bleach is to diseased bacteria, Christ's perfect righteousness is to sin's defilement. Once transferred, the sin of the world could not defile or render Christ guilty any more than my pouring bacteria into a bucket of bleach renders the bleach diseased. The nature of bleach is to kill infection, *not become infected.*

How does all this relate to us? In every way! It paves the way for us to be purified and pardoned—i.e. cleansed and forgiven.

Purification and *pardon,* not payment and punishment

In every offense there is the offender and the offended. In the case of sin, it is not only a horizontal offense against our neighbors, but a vertical one. We have sinned against God. In the O.T., sacrifices were offered to atone for sins by the *offending* party—sinners. They were not offered by the *offended* party—God. However, in the N.T., this too gets reversed. Although our sins certainly *offended* God, we discover that God (the One offended) is offering up Christ as "the atoning sacrifice for our sins" (1 John 2:2 NIV).

Not as *payment* to Himself was Christ given by the Father, but as *purification* for us. The blood of Christ covers us—atones—in the sense that it represents the purity of Christ's life being given to us for our purification. Knowing this to be the case, John states, "...the blood of Jesus... cleanses us from all sin" (1 John 1:7).

The imagery is powerful because blood doesn't literally *clean* anything, but *stains* everything. However, we are not in the realm of soap and bubbles, but soul and spirit. Very early on in redemptive history, we read God saying, "...the life of a creature is in the blood, and I have appointed it to you to make atonement..." (Leviticus 17:11).

In other words—blood represents life. Recall what we learned earlier. Sin's very nature is anti-life because it relationally severs us from the source of life itself—God.

In Christ, God's plan is to reconcile a dying humanity to Him by having the purity of Christ's sinless life absorb the full force of our sinful defilement and carry it into death once and for all. With this knowledge in mind, we can now better appreciate the fact that to speak of the "blood of Christ" is to essentially speak of the purity of His righteous life being given to "cleanse our conscience" (Hebrews 9:14).

We are now entering the realm of forgiveness or pardon. To be pardoned means to be released from condemnation for wrongdoing.

"Therefore, no condemnation now exits"

Based on what Christ has done, we are declared to be on the side of life and no longer under sin's condemnation. The "law of sin and death" has been replaced with a new law—the law of life. Paul ties in the Holy Spirit into this incredible, Triune work of liberation, proclaiming, **"Therefore, no condemnation now exists for those in Christ Jesus because the Spirit's law of life** has set you free from the law of sin and death" (Romans 8:1–2).

This is the essence of the biblical doctrine of justification. We are judicially declared to be in the right— no longer under sin's condemnation.

Like a hub at the center of a wheel, every theological "spoke" connects back to the central act of God disarming Satan's "weaponization" of sin by condemning sin *in Christ* so that it could no longer condemn us *in Christ.*

Looking at the cross through this "lens" allows the true nature of our pardon from sin to come into focus. To the extent God judged the sin of the world "to be in the wrong" in Christ, is to the extent we can say God's justice was *satisfied.* This in turn paved the way forward for us to be pardoned and forgiven—to be "put in the right" (made righteous and justified).

"For God did not send His Son into the world, that He might condemn the world, but that the world might be saved **through Him**," (John 3:17) is how Christ spoke of His mission. Clearly, He saw His life acting like a grace-filled pardon from God to us.

But pardons can be rejected, which is why Christ went on to declare, "Anyone who believes in Him is not condemned, but anyone who does not believe is already condemned, because he has not believed in the name of the One and Only Son of God" (verse 18).

To reject a pardon is to remain in one's own sins—to insist on paying sin's wages on your own! It is to reject the very One sent from above to separate you from sin's condemnation. This is precisely why Jesus warned the religious Pharisees, saying,

> "You are from below... I am from above. You are of this world; I am not of this world. Therefore, I told you that you will die in your sins. For if you do not believe that I am He, **you will die in your**

sins" (John 8:23–24). [*Both belief and disbelief in Christ assumes sufficient knowledge of Christ was available. Questions related to those who lack knowledge of Christ is beyond the scope of this book, but a brief outline is sketched in endnote 2*].

Viewing God's forgiveness through the lens of a grace-filled pardon also relates to the holy nature of Divine wrath and God's desire to send the Son on a mission to save humanity from their unholy state. For instance, concerning the arrival of the Messiah on earth, John the Baptist proclaimed,

> "The One who comes from above is above all...For God sent Him...The Father loves the Son and has given all things into His hands. The one who believes in the Son has eternal life, but **the one who refuses to believe in the Son** will not see life; instead, **the wrath of God remains on him**" (John 3:31-36).

If the Son was sent to divorce us from our sins and marry us to His life (reconciliation), then to willfully reject the Son is to reverse this order. It is to divorce ourselves from God's life and re-marry ourselves *back* to the very sins God condemned in the *sinless* perfection of His Son. Therefore, to say "the wrath of God remains" on someone is to say a person has chosen to have their sinful lives examined and judged by the full intensity of God's holiness (i.e. wrath) *without* adequate covering— without perfect atonement.

In the most basic sense, it means one has chosen to refuse God's pardoning grace by rejecting God's declaration that their sins were judged to be "in the wrong." Why? Because through their unwillingness to repent, they have declared to God that their sins are "in the right." This is both the essence and danger of maintaining an unrepentant heart. The end result is to place ourselves *back* under sin's condemnation, and therefore *back* under God's morally good opposition to all that is not good—His wrath. This leads to our last and final point—a very critical point.

Woe to those who try to *justify* what God has *condemned*

Paul made it clear that God's pardoning grace is not a license to practice sin without consequence (Romans 6:1). Satan also knows this, which is why he is not lying down "licking his wounds" in defeat. As was mentioned in our story, the serpentine *nachash* aims to recapture as many victims as he can through deception and poisonous lies. A powerful deception Satan employs is to ensnare people into thinking they can *justify* their sin rather than *repent* of it. Woe to the one who thinks they can remain in God's pardon while knowingly justifying their sin.

Just think about it. If the triumph of the cross over powers of darkness was accomplished by God condemning sin, then to justify sin's continued presence in our lives, rather than confessing it and repenting from it, is the most foolish thing one can do. We are not talking about an honest, common struggle with sin. We are talking about an unrepentant justification of sin—granting it permission to remain with us. To try and justify "in Christ" what God has condemned "in Christ" is the pinnacle of arrogance. It is to forfeit Christ's pardon and retain one's sins.

In short, we can neither enter into Christ's pardon, nor remain in Christ's pardon while simultaneously believing our sins are justified to remain in us. We cannot have it both ways. We must repent.

The Gospel is indeed good news, but if the Gospel hasn't yet offended our sense of self-justification—then we haven't yet heard the Gospel. The Gospel message begins hearing God say, "Your sins have put you *in the wrong*." Only then can we hear God say, "But I have come to put you *in the right*."

Summary conclusion

Being both the divine Son of God and the perfect man, Jesus Christ stood in the gap between the living and the dead, between heaven and earth, between God and humanity and said, "I will absorb sin-soaked humanity into Myself. My life will cleanse all image bearers and they shall come through Me redeemed and reconciled."

Shall we risk another analogy? Yes. Like contaminated, toxic blood being run through a dialysis machine, sin-soaked humanity, starting with Adam, was absorbed into Christ's perfect, righteous nature and cleansed by His sinless life. It is no wonder Paul summarized Christ's ministry of death and resurrection for the world as follows: "For as in Adam all die, so in Christ all will be made alive" (1 Corinthians 15:22).

Christ's arrival on earth signaled the arrival of God's kingdom and the overthrow of Satan's kingdom. A new day was dawning on earth, for the "Light of the World" had come. The light of that new day was going to grow ever brighter. On the cross, with the Son of God stripped naked and hanging by nails, it momentarily appeared as if the light of that dawning day was going to be swallowed up in darkness and humiliating defeat.

But what at first appeared to be victory for the powers of darkness ended up being the cause of their doom and defeat. For unbeknownst to them, Christ's faithful obedience unto death was overthrowing their dark kingdom by depriving them of access to humanity's sins through which they held men and women enslaved to sin's condemnation and consequence—death.

For this reason, we are told "through death" Jesus ransacked the dominion of darkness to "destroy the one who has the power of death, that is, the devil, and deliver all those who through fear of death were subject to lifelong slavery" (Hebrews 2:14–15).

The "light" of the rising sun, the new day dawning, was at its highest point in the sky on Resurrection morning, when the Rising Son stepped out of the grave and sentenced death to death. No wonder Christ declared in Revelation, "Don't be afraid! I am the First and the Last, and the Living One. I was dead, but look—I am alive forever and ever, and I hold the keys of death and Hades" (Revelation 1:17–18).

Prayer of Closing

"May we continue to praise You, Almighty God, for Your wonderful and mysterious plan of redemption that liberated us from sin and the powers of darkness. May You grant us wisdom and strength to become Your disciples—deputies of Your authority and ambassadors of Your love and light. Amen."

About the author

 Matt Bohlman has an M.A. in Religion from Liberty Theological Seminary. He has worked in Cambodia as a Christian humanitarian for over 10 years with the NGO People for Care and Learning. Much of his time was spent overseeing an orphanage of amazing kids. He currently lectures on biblical studies in S.E. Asia and helps to fund various projects and educational scholarships. He enjoys sipping coffee while planning out his next book—or he could be daydreaming. Sometimes they merge together. He is an aspiring author and can be reached at: mattbohlmanbooks@gmail.com

***If this book has encouraged you, please consider writing a short review on Amazon.com. Simply type the author's name in the Amazon search box and the book will pop up. Scroll down to "Write a review" and click on the link to share your thoughts.
THANKS!***

Endnotes

[1] There is a sense in which Christ's death and resurrection "delivers us from the wrath to come" (1 Thessalonians 1:10). But Paul is careful to put God's wrath in the future tense. Paul is *not* looking back at the cross in this passage. Paul is talking about a future day that goes by many names in Scripture—one of them is "the day of the Lord." The nature of God's wrath as it pertains to the future day of God's glory and holiness being

revealed without any filters (as with Moses in Exodus 33:22) will be explored in a forthcoming book titled: *Perfectus Liberatio.*

2 Many often wonder what happens to those who never hear the gospel—or who heard a distorted, blasphemous version of it (i.e., at the point of a crusader sword). Is it at least *possible* such people can still come through the atonement of Christ and be saved on the final day when "God judges the secrets of men..." (Rm. 2:16)? It is beyond the scope of this book to fully address this valid question. But the short answer is—yes, it is possible! For example, we know for a fact that all Old Testament saints who lacked conscious knowledge of Christ will nonetheless come through Christ's atonement in the future resurrection. This will include non-Israelites like Melchizedek and Job, as well as Gentiles "without the law" whose conscience Paul says may "accuse or **even excuse** them" on the final day (Rm. 2:15). A teaching that is often repeated in many different ways throughout Scripture is that God only holds people accountable to the measure of what they have been given. This includes the measure of light and special revelation they have received concerning God. This does not result in a disincentive for missions or evangelism because in the "economy" of God's justice, the ratio between revelation and response is always 1:1. We see this proportional ratio between what is given and what is required in the parable of the talents. The one who received 2 talents only needed to demonstrate a proportional response of 2 more. He did not need to respond with 5 more, as was the case with the servant before him. Likewise, the one who received the greater measure of 5 talents *would have* been judged unfaithful *if* he only responded with 2 more talents (Mt. 25:14-30). In addition, Christ declared that those who are ignorant of the Master's will shall not be judged to the same degree as those who have knowledge of the Master's will (Lk. 12:47). The Pharisees were not

judged because they were spiritually blind. Instead, Jesus said their judgement was self-inflicted, for they arrogantly refused to concede they were blind and needed His light. "If you were blind," Jesus told them, "you wouldn't have sin. But now that you say, 'We see'--your sin remains" (Jn. 9:41). None of this should be taken to mean "ignorance is bliss" and missions should be discontinued. Our job is to be faithful witnesses and carriers of the light of God's kingdom in Christ. Only God can make the final judgment that evaluates how people responded to the "talents" of light and grace they were given. A more robust explanation of these issues will have to await another day.

3 The Bible treats death as a personalized enemy whose final ruin is yet in the future. Speaking of Christ's reign over all things, Paul says, "For He must reign until He puts all His enemies under His feet. The last enemy to be abolished is death" (1 Corinthians 15:25–26). In speaking of this future day, John writes, "Death and Hades were thrown into the lake of fire. This is the second death..."(Revelation 20:14).

Made in the
USA
Middletown, DE